Colin G. Carnie

"I find that although few of my friends are good mathematicians many are good bookkeepers."

Cairnvor,
Kilmacolm.

THE DESIGN AND TUNING
OF COMPETITION ENGINES

The Design and Tuning of Competition Engines

by

PHILIP H. SMITH, A.M.I.Mech.E.

Chartered Mechanical Engineer
Chartered Automobile Engineer
Technical Editor "Motor Racing"

LONDON
G. T. FOULIS & CO. LTD.
7 Milford Lane, Strand, W.C.2

PRINTED BY THE MARSHALL PRESS LIMITED, MILFORD LANE, STRAND, LONDON, W.C.2.

CONTENTS

PART I

HIGH EFFICIENCY ENGINE DESIGN

Page

INTRODUCTION 14

Chapter

1. HEAT ENGINE OPERATION 16

    First principles—The specific heat of air—Expansion and compression—Air standard efficiency—Indicated and brake horsepower—Mechanical efficiency—Factors governing expansion pressure—Calculating thermal efficiency

2. THE PRODUCTION OF POWER 27

    B.m.e.p. and torque—Power production—Compression ratio and detonation—Pressure increase with compression ratio—Heat loss—Water temperature—Valve size and gas velocity

3. PROBLEMS OF CYLINDER CHARGING 36

    Valve timing—Maximum charging—Overlap snags—High-speed operation—Pulsating pressure—High power; narrow speed range—Application to multi-cylinder engines—Exhaust systems

4. MECHANICAL CONSTRUCTION OF HIGH-POWER ENGINES 47

    Basic materials in construction—Non-ferrous materials—Fatigue failure—Valve operation—Twin o.h.c. engines—Single o.h.c. engines—Crankshafts—Bearings and materials

5. CRANKSHAFT DESIGN 63

    Bearing location—Problems of balancing—Secondary forces—Balancing the single—Sixes and eights—Vibration dampers—Bore-stroke ratio

5

Contents *(continued)*

Chapter   *Page*

6. PLANNING FOR PERFORMANCE   72

*Performance data—Cylinder head design—Efficient scavenging—
Overhead valve layouts—Compression ratio and heat loss—
Turbulence features with o.h.v. head—A popular type—Considerations of gas flow—O.h. inlet, side exhaust valve arrangements—The inclined-o.h.v. combustion chamber—High compression ratios—Spark plug position*

7. COMBUSTION CHAMBER LAYOUT   102

*Improving performance—Breathing—Inlet valve size—Inlet port
characteristics—Combustion chamber requirements—Exhaust
pressure—The influence of plug position—Ignition current—
Coils and plugs*

8. A HIGH-GRADE DESIGN—THE ASTON MARTIN   ... 114

*Power output—The crankshaft assembly—Cylinder head and valve
gear—The lubrication system—The cooling system*

9. POWER PER C.C.—THE BRISTOL   121

*High output—The crankcase assembly—Connecting rods and
pistons—Camshaft and valve gear—The cylinder head—The
lubrication and cooling systems—Further developments*

10. RUGGED SIMPLICITY—THE FORD   128

*The " Prefect " — Crankcase assembly — Connecting rods and
pistons—Valve gear—The lubrication system—The ignition
system—The " Consul " and " Zephyr "—Crankshaft assembly—
Connecting rods and pistons—Cylinder head and valve gear—
Lubrication and cooling systems*

11. CLASSIC LAYOUT—THE JAGUAR   139

*Power output—The crankcase assembly—Cylinder head and valve
gear—Auxiliary drives—The cooling system*

12. BREAK WITH THE ORTHODOX—THE JOWETT   ... 145

*The flat-four—Crankcase assembly—Connecting rods and pistons
—Cylinder heads and valve gear—The lubrication system—
Auxiliary drives—The R4 engine*

6

Contents (continued)

Chapter	Page
13. A Big Four—The Lea-Francis	151

A long-stroke unit—The valve gear—The main casting—Connecting rods and pistons—Auxiliary drives—The lubrication system

14. Power Without Frills—The M.G.	159

A simple o.h.v. design—The main assembly—Connecting rods and pistons—The cylinder head and valve gear—The lubrication system—Auxiliary drives—The type TF engine

PART 2

TUNING AND MODIFYING FOR PERFORMANCE

	Page
Introduction	168

Chapter	
15. The Cylinder Head...	170

Some general points—Improving volumetric efficiency—The inlet tract—Oversize valves—Attention to the exhaust side—Valves, springs and collars—Exhaust pipe layout

16. Modifications to Valve Gear	198

Rocker accuracy—Rocker-shaft details—Cam followers—Modifications to standard timing—Lightening tappets

17. Attention to Cylinders and Pistons	205

Exacting clearances—Piston rings—Gas leakage—Piston design—Connecting rods—Correcting errors

18. Choice of Compression Ratio	213

Raising the ratio—Obtaining head volume—Valve clearance—Special pistons—The cylinder-head joint

Contents (continued)

Chapter		Page
19.	TUNING THE FORD TEN	219

An attractive engine—"Aquaplane" modifications—Tuning in six stages—Racing equipment—Specialists' recommendations—Volumetric efficiency—Ignition equipment—Sprint racing

| 20. | TUNING THE JAGUAR ... ... | 232 |

The XK120 engine—Fitting special camshafts—Raising the compression ratio—Other items—The chassis—Specials parts list

| 21. | TUNING THE JOWETT ... ... | 238 |

General work—Cylinder heads and ports—Compression ratio—Bearings — Carburetters — Other engine fittings — Transmission —Parts available for modifications

| 22. | TUNING THE M.G. ... ... | 247 |

The standard engine—Tuning in five stages—General observations

| 23. | MISCELLANEOUS ENGINE TUNING ... ... | 257 |

The A.C.—Ford o.h.v. engines—The s.v. Morris Minor—Sunbeam-Talbot

| 24. | RATIONAL SUPERCHARGING ... ... | 262 |

Objects of forced induction—Supercharger design—Comparison of types—Performance of blown engines

| 25. | APPENDICES ... ... | 272 |

Definitions—Abbreviations—Useful constants and formulae—Design data of British competition engines—Directory of suppliers

LIST OF ILLUSTRATIONS

	Page
The 500-c.c. Norton intake and exhaust branches ...	81
Reverse-cone megaphone on tailpipe of 500-c.c. racing car	81
The timing drive of the XK120 Jaguar	82
The timing drive of the 2½-litre Riley	83
Fracture of a valve-rocker	84
Aston Martin crankshaft	84
„ „ crankcase	84
„ „ engine, nearside	85
„ „ „ offside	85
100/B engine which powers the Bristol 404 Sports coupé	86
Inlet rockers on Bristol engine	86
The Bristol 2-litre engine, type 100/A	87
„ „ „ „ „ 85/A	87
A cut-away view of the 1,172-c.c. Ford engine	88
Ford " Consul " manifold layout	88
„ „ cylinder block and head	89
„ " Prefect " 1,172-c.c. engine, nearside	89
Nearside view of Ford " Consul " engine	90
Jaguar combustion chambers	90
„ cylinder head	90
The seven main bearing housings of the Jaguar XK120 engine	91
Jaguar camshaft and associated components	91
The 3½-litre Jaguar XK120, offside	92
„ „ „ „ nearside	92
The Lea-Francis rocker gear	93
„ „ crankcase and cylinder block casting ...	93
The 2½-litre Lea-Francis engine, offside	94
On the Lea-Francis, different heights of piston crown ...	94
The 2½-litre Lea-Francis engine, nearside	95
The Lea-Francis combustion chambers	95
The chain drive to twin camshafts on the 2½-litre Lea-Francis engine	96
Mr. V. A. Fox's manifold conversion for a Ford " Consul " engine. Two carburetters are accommodated ...	177
Mr. V. A. Fox's manifold conversion on the Ford " Consul " engine	177

9

Page

Mr. V. A. Fox's conversion on the Ford " Consul " engine 178
Exhibition model of Ford 10 engine, fitted up with
    Aquaplane equipment 178
The Davies Special intake and exhaust manifold for the
    Ford 1,172-c.c. engine 179
Aquaplane alloy timing case cover for Ford 10 179
Aquaplane alloy racing flywheel for Ford 10 180
Aquaplane alloy cylinder head for Ford 10, with normal
    position for water take-off 180
Aquaplane alloy cylinder head for Ford 10, with end
    take-off for water 180
Aquaplane 900/2 S.U.K. manifold for Ford 10 181
Aquaplane manifold 900/2ZB for Ford 10 181
    ,,   ,,   900/2ZK for standard Ford 10 car-
    buretter 182
The 2½-litre Riley engine 182
1,250-c.c. M.G. type TD engine, offside 183
    ,,   ,,   ,,   ,,   nearside 183
The Laystall alloy cylinder head for M.G. engines ... 184
An alloy rocker-box design by the author 184
The Austin A40 exhibition engine, sectioned to show
    components 185
An effective four carburetter induction layout on the
    1,100-c.c. Riley engine 186
A Riley 1,100-c.c. engine 186
The Davies Special manifold for the s.v. Morris Minor ... 187
The Raymond Mays three carburetter induction system
    for the Ford " Zephyr " engine 187
The Jowett flat-four engine 188
The Shorrock supercharger installation on the Mark II
    o.h.v. Morris Minor 188
The Shorrock supercharger installation on the Mark II
    o.h.v. 800-c.c. Morris Minor 189
Internal arrangement of Shorrock supercharger (type C
    142B) 189
The Shorrock supercharger installation on series M.M.
    side valve Morris Minor 190
Exploded view of a Wade blower 191
The Wade supercharger installation fitted to an M.G.
    type TC engine 191
The Shorrock supercharger on the TD M.G. 192

FOREWORD

This book has been written for motoring enthusiasts who take an interest in competition-type cars in general and in the design, modification and tuning of power units in particular, whether the object be actual participation in motoring sport, or merely that of obtaining the best possible performance for normal occasions.

Its contents, therefore, are not exclusively concerned with what are commonly known as high-efficiency engines, since many successful cars use engines originally designed for the most economical form of personal transport. These have shown themselves capable of being reliably tuned and modified to achieve remarkable increases of power output.

Almost without exception, the enthusiast for motoring as a sport and pastime is commendably knowledgeable regarding the operation of his machine, and the significance of various points of design. To obtain the utmost satisfaction out of ownership of a sporting type of vehicle, however, the more that is known about it, and about contemporary designs, the better. This is particularly applicable when modifications aimed at increased performance are being contemplated.

An understanding of the theory of heat engine operation is invaluable in enabling many pitfalls to be avoided, particularly in respect of alterations to the " combustion " side of the engine. Adequate space has therefore been devoted in the first part of the book to an explanation of basic theory, without becoming too involved or introducing irrelevant considerations.

In dealing with practical modifications to existing engines of various makes, the author has been impressed by the very genuine enthusiasm shown by relatively small engineering concerns of a specialist type. Car makers have also, in general, co-operated well, the exceptions in this category being, curiously enough, names which, before they became " big business," were amongst those most revered by sporting motorists !

ACKNOWLEDGMENT

The Author would like to express his appreciation of the valued co-operation of the following in supplying photographs and other data without which this book would be far from complete:—

The Editors and Staff of *The Automobile Engineer*, *Motor Trader*, *The Autocar*, *The Motor*, *Autosport*, and *Motoring*. The manufacturers of A.C., Bristol, Ford, Jaguar, Jowett, Lea-Francis and M.G. cars. Laystall Engineering Co. Ltd.; The Renold and Coventry Chain Co. Ltd.; Shorrock Superchargers Ltd.; Wade Engineering Ltd.; Mr. H. H. F. Copeman of The Aquaplane Co., Oulton Broad; Mr. C. D. F. Buckler of Bucklers, Reading; Mr. O. H. J. Davies of Castle Garage, Pembroke; Mr. V. A. Fox of Central Garage, Bangor; Mr. B. T. Pritchard Lovell of Geo. Hartwell Ltd., Bournemouth; Mr. Raymond Mays; and many other good people for their help and encouragement.

The author is especially grateful to the Editor of *The Automobile Engineer*, and Lea-Francis Cars Ltd. for the use of the engine drawing which forms the background of the jacket of this book.

BROOKLANDS, MANCHESTER.
December, 1953.

PART I

HIGH EFFICIENCY ENGINE DESIGN

			Page
Introduction	... ...		14
Chapter 1.	Heat Engine Operation		16
„ 2.	The Production of Power		27
„ 3.	Problems of Cylinder Charging		36
„ 4.	Mechanical Construction of High-power Engines		47
„ 5.	Crankshaft Design		63
„ 6.	Planning for Performance		72
„ 7.	Combustion Chamber Layout		102
„ 8.	A High-grade Design—The Aston Martin		114
„ 9.	Power per c.c.—The Bristol		121
„ 10.	Rugged Simplicity—The Ford		128
„ 11.	Classic Layout—The Jaguar		139
„ 12.	Break with the Orthodox—The Jowett ...		145
„ 13.	A Big Four—The Lea-Francis		151
„ 14.	Power Without Frills—The M.G. ...		159

Introduction to Part 1

In order to appreciate the reasons which lead designers to adopt certain constructional features, and in particular to sum up the significance of various forms of valve gear, combustion chamber layout, choice of compression ratio, bore-stroke ratio, and so on, it is desirable that an intelligent grasp is obtained of the principles governing the operation of heat engines. Such knowledge is still more important when modifications and tuning operations are being considered. It is, of course, frequently possible to improve the performance of an engine (and quite often to mar it) merely by following blindly the advice which is available from many sources, usually dealing with such severely practical matters as raising the compression ratio or fitting larger valves.

All other things being equal, however, the man who knows even in general what the designer of his engine had in mind when choosing that particular layout, and who has a clear idea of what to expect if he carries out certain proposals of his own, will be a jump ahead of the enthusiast who shaves a fraction of his cylinder head because someone else did so. Although to some the science of thermodynamics may appear involved, the rules applicable to production of power in the type of engine with which we are concerned are relatively simple, and can be explained without undue complication. This is not an attempt to play down the technical aspect, as obviously these things require study. However, once the principles are grasped firmly, they need never be forgotten, and the knowledge will enable the reader to take with a pinch of salt statements that he might previously have accepted as gospel. He will also be enabled to look at the various " modern " improvements in design which crop up from time to time, in the right perspective.

In detailing the constructional features of well-known power units, an endeavour has been made to select examples which typify current practice in engines used in all forms of competition work. There are, of course, several other successful makes apart from those described, but in most if not all cases their design features will be found to follow one or other of the examples chosen.

In assessing the merits or otherwise of various designs, after considering what is desirable from the theoretical point of view, the matter of production cost should not be forgotten. Most engineering is a compromise. Even to-day the modern competition type engine may on occasion display features which make the owner wonder what the designer was thinking about, but it will usually be found that he had a very good reason for doing what he did, though such reason may not, of course, be at all convincing to the user of the product.

CHAPTER I

Heat Engine Operation

*First principles—The specific heat of air—Expansion and compression—
Air standard efficiency—Indicated and brake horse-power—
Mechanical efficiency—Factors governing expansion pressure—
Calculating thermal efficiency*

First principles

The internal combustion engine depends for its operation
on the expansion of gases in the working cylinders. These
gases are affected by temperature, pressure and change of
volume, the three items being inter-related in a manner which,
when fully understood, renders the calculation of various
factors influencing engine power output and fuel consumption,
relatively simple.

The " gas " with which we are concerned consists mainly
of atmospheric air to which a percentage of fuel vapour is
added to produce a combustible mixture. This mixture obeys
closely the various laws relating to gases, which will now be
detailed.

The first law, due to Robert Boyle, states that, assuming
the gas temperature is kept constant, the volume will vary
inversely as its pressure. In other words, if we compress the
gas, at unvarying temperature and at a certain original
pressure, into half its original volume or space, its pressure
will become double the original. Thus, if P = pressure, and
V = volume, we can say

$$PV = \text{a constant.}$$

The second law, by the French scientist Charles, states
that the volume of a quantity of gas varies 1/273 of its volume
at o deg. C. for every 1 deg. C. change in temperature (or,
using the Fahrenheit scale, 1/492 for every 1 deg. F.), always
providing the pressure is kept constant. This is based on the
assumption that at the " absolute zero " temperature of

16

−273 deg. C., the volume would become zero. In practice, of course, gases, when cooled beyond a certain point, liquefy and finally solidify.

What Charles's law tells us is that the gas volume increases by equal increments for equal increases in temperature. As the volume is proportional to the absolute temperature, we can say, with V = volume and T = temperature,

$$\frac{V}{T} = \text{a constant.}$$

From the foregoing, it will be apparent that if the gas is in a closed cylinder and unable to expand, thus keeping the volume constant and unaltered, any application of heat will alter its pressure, in proportion to the rise in temperature. Thus, we can say

$$\frac{P}{T} = \text{a constant.}$$

Therefore, since PV and $\frac{P}{T}$ both equal a constant, we can combine the two and obtain $\frac{PV}{T}$ = a constant for any one particular gas.

This relationship between P, T, and V will obtain throughout the operating cycle and, of course, works both ways, that is, whether the heat is added or taken away, and whether the pressure or volume, or both, are increasing or decreasing.

The specific heat of air

In actual engines, air forms the bulk of the working mixture, and therefore the behaviour of air when subjected to the changing conditions of the operating cycle of the engine forms a useful guide to engine performance.

There are two values of specific heat for air; one is obtained with the air at constant pressure, and the other with the air at constant volume.

B

At constant pressure, the specific heat of dry air is taken as ·2374 B.Th.U. per lb. weight. If a quantity of air is allowed to expand as its temperature rises, in accordance with Charles's law, it will do work by exerting pressure against the surrounding atmosphere. Taking the quantity of air as 1 lb. in weight, its volume at normal temperature and pressure will be 12.387 cu. ft. If its temperature is raised by 1 deg. F., it will expand by 1/492 of its volume against atmospheric pressure. Now, assuming atmospheric pressure as 14.7 lb. per sq. in., that is equal to 14.7 × 144 lb. per sq. ft. Multiply this by the volume of 12.387 cu. ft., and then by 1/492. This gives the work done against the atmosphere in foot-pounds.

Thus:
$$\frac{14.7 \times 144 \times 12.387}{492} = 53.29 \text{ ft.-lb.}$$

To convert this to B.Th.U., we divide it by 778.

Thus:
$$\frac{53.29}{778} = .0685 \text{ B.Th.U.}$$

If the air is not allowed to expand against atmospheric pressure, that is, the volume is maintained unaltered, the pressure of the air will rise, but there will be no external work performed. The specific heat required (.2374 B.Th.U. per lb. at constant pressure) will therefore, at constant volume, be less by the amount calculated above, that is,

$$.2374 - .0685 = .1689 \text{ B.Th.U.}$$

It will thus be seen that there are two values of specific heat for air:

At constant pressure   ...   .2374 B.Th.U. per lb.
At constant volume   ...   .1689 B.Th.U. per lb.

The relationship between the two values is very important in engine calculations. It is referred to by the Greek letter Gamma, written γ. By simple calculation, it will be seen that, for air,

$$\gamma = \frac{.2374}{.1689} = 1.406.$$

Expansion and compression

In practice, the conditions under which expansion and compression take place are quite complicated.   It is, however, feasible to classify these operations into two forms, namely, Isothermal and Adiabatic.

Isothermal expansion or compression assumes that Boyle's law is faithfully followed, and thus that no change in temperature takes place.   This would mean that during expansion under constant temperature, the internal energy of the air would also remain unchanged, since this is proportional to the absolute temperature.   The work necessary for expansion would thus have to be supplied from a source of external heat.

Again, during isothermal compression, the heat generated in the air would have to be allowed to escape as quickly as it was generated, and the heat flowing away during compression

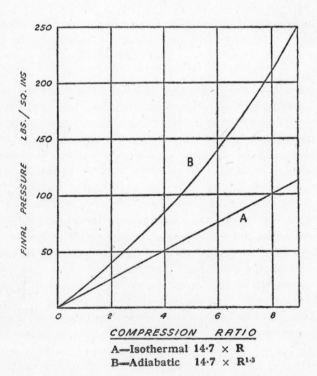

A—Isothermal 14·7 × R
B—Adiabatic   14·7 × R$^{1·3}$

would be equal to the heat supplied from outside during expansion.

Adiabatic expansion or compression assumes that no heat flows either to or from the air during the operation. Thus, the air would gain or lose internal energy, as the temperature is raised by compression and lowered by expansion, and the amount of internal energy is proportional to the quantity of external work done by or put into it.

Now, to get back for a moment to the isothermal condition; supposing the original volume V is compressed to a smaller volume V_1, the original pressure P will rise to a pressure P_1, so that we obtain

$$PV = P_1V_1 = \text{a constant.}$$

If, however, we carry out the operation adiabatically, the equation becomes

$$PV^n = P_1V_1{}^n$$

With isothermal conditions, $n = 1$, as the internal energy of the air is unchanged. Under adiabatic operation, the air gains or loses internal energy, and thus n is equal to γ, or to 1.406.

In actual practice, the value of n lies somewhere between 1 and 1.406, as it is dependent on the characteristics of such items as the fuel added to form a combustible mixture, and the conditions of heat flow in the engine. If mixture is admitted, for instance, to the cylinder of an engine which is already warm through running, heat will flow from the cylinder to the mixture, and thus in the early stages, including the first part of the compression stroke, this heat will continue to flow.

Temporarily, therefore, n will exceed the normal value of γ. However, as the mixture temperature proceeds quickly to equal and then to exceed the cylinder temperature as compression continues, the heat flow will first stop and then reverse direction, so that at the latter stages, heat will be lost from the mixture to the cylinder walls: n will then fall below γ, to an amount dependent on the temperature difference between gas and metal. This will obviously be influenced by the area of metal exposed to the gas, the ratio between volume and internal surfaces, the density and amount of movement of the gas, and so on. It will be evident that the higher the piston speed, the less time there will be for heat transfer to take place.

Air Standard Efficiency

Based on the foregoing, we can calculate a useful efficiency figure for what might be called a " perfect " engine. This figure is known as the Air Standard Efficiency, or a.s.e., and is actually the thermal efficiency of an engine assumed to be burning air only, with $n = 1.406$.

In calculating a.s.e., we assume that both the induction and exhaust strokes take place at atmospheric pressure; that adiabatic conditions apply on compression and expansion strokes; and that all heat received from " outside " by the air is received at the top of the compression stroke instantaneously, with the air at constant volume.

Under those conditions, the air standard efficiency is given by the formula:

$$\text{a.s.e.} = 1 - \left(\frac{1}{r}\right)^{\gamma - 1}$$

As, with air, γ is equal to 1.406 (usually shortened to 1.4), the formula becomes:

$$\text{a.s.e.} = 1 - \left(\frac{1}{r}\right)^{0.4}$$

Where $r =$ the compression ratio.

The a.s.e. shows us what percentage of the external heat added to the air is converted into work. (In practice, of course, this heat is produced by combining the air with fuel to form a combustible mixture.) It will be evident from a study of the above formula that the compression ratio governs the a.s.e. and that the higher the value of r, the greater the a.s.e. The value of being able to work out the a.s.e. for any particular engine lies in the fact that it forms a yardstick against which the results obtained in practice can be assessed. The corresponding figure obtained on the test bed is known as the Thermal Efficiency.

We are not concerned with compression ratios below about 6 : 1, and thus the following table plotting a.s.e. against r, commences at this ratio.

Air Standard Efficiency, per cent.

r	eff.			r	eff.
6.0	51.16	...	...	7.5	55.34
6.2	51.8	...	...	8.0	56.47
6.4	52.38	...	...	9.0	57.4
6.6	53.0	...	...	10.0	60.2
6.8	53.55	...	...	11.0	61.7
7.0	53.98	...	...	12.0	62.9

To the designer, a.s.e. represents what might be called the overall efficiency of the " upper-works " of the engine considered as an apparatus for converting the heat energy contained in the fuel into work on the pistons. If he chooses a compression ratio of 7.5 : 1, the " perfect " engine would convert over 55 per cent. of the fuel energy into power. The nearer the actual thermal efficiency obtained can be made to approach this figure, the more power will be produced per unit of fuel mixture delivered to the inlet valves, and the more can the designer congratulate himself on his port, valve, cylinder and head layout. But power is not the only point to consider. Another important item is that any heat liberated in the mixture which is not converted into work has somehow to be got rid of.

Indicated and Brake Horse-power

It is expected that most readers will be familiar with the definitions of the above two terms. However, it will be useful to continue by detailing them.

Indicated horse-power (i.h.p.) represents the h.p. produced on the pistons, and is calculated from the cylinder expansion pressure, which is measured by a device called an indicator—hence the name. This pressure is stated as mean effective pressure, or m.e.p., in lb. per sq. in. In obtaining it, the pressures throughout the cycle are used, and in each case the pressure is the average, or mean, obtaining on that particular stroke. An example will explain matters.

Assuming that atmospheric pressure is 15 lb. per sq. in.
Induction pressure say 12 lb. per sq. in. (absolute.)

Compression ,, ,, 40 ,, ,, ,,
Expansion ,, ,, 185 ,, ,, ,,
Exhaust ,, ,, 18 ,, ,, ,,

The expansion pressure is the only positive stroke, the other three being employed in pumping work, or negatively. Thus the *effective* pressure is 185−(12+40+18) or 115 lb. per sq. in.

If, having obtained the pressure on the pistons, we combine with this the distance and time factors required, we can obtain a result in ft.-lb. per min., and thus h.p.

If p = expansion pressure (i.m.e.p.) in lb. per sq. in.
    l = length of stroke in feet.
    a = area of one piston in sq. in.
    n = number of working (expansion) strokes per minute of engine;

then multiplication of the above four quantities will give the result in ft.-lb. per min. If this is divided by 33,000, the result will give i.h.p.

Therefore   i.h.p. $= \dfrac{p \times l \times a \times n}{33,000}$

Brake horse-power (b.h.p.) is the actual power available at the engine crankshaft or flywheel, and is so called because in the early days it was measured by applying a braking force to a pulley or drum on the engine-shaft. Modern " brakes," though still freely called by that name, are actually known as dynamometers, and the power is absorbed electrically or hydraulically.

Mechanical efficiency

Since i.h.p. represents the power at the engine pistons, and b.h.p. the power at the crankshaft, it follows that the difference in the two values is caused by the mechanical losses consequent in converting the expansion pressure to rotating motion. The percentage of i.h.p. available as b.h.p. is known as the mechanical efficiency, and is obviously obtained thus:

$$\text{Mechanical eff. (per cent.)} = \frac{\text{b.h.p.}}{\text{i.h.p.}}$$

It will be appreciated that the losses aforementioned include not only piston and bearing friction, but also the power required to drive the valve gear, ignition apparatus, oil-pump, and other incidentals.

Factors governing expansion pressure

The expansion pressure depends in general on the quantity of charge introduced into the cylinder, on the efficiency of its conversion to work on the piston, and on the percentage of the charge that is actually so converted. These three factors are known respectively as volumetric efficiency, combustion efficiency, and thermal efficiency.

It is usual to combine all the above three factors in one efficiency figure, as thermal efficiency, and on engine test runs the mechanical efficiency is also usually combined with them, the resulting overall figure being known as brake thermal efficiency. This useful figure shows the merits of the engine in regard to its ability to convert fuel heat energy into crank-shaft b.h.p., and is obviously a most important one.

It will be appreciated that the indicated thermal efficiency is the practical counterpart of air standard efficiency, and useful information can be obtained by comparing the two. In practice, of course, the figure obtained on test is considerably lower than the a.s.e. for equivalent compression ratio. There are several reasons for this, notably:—

(a) γ is less than 1.4 due to the necessity for mixing fuel with the air.

(b) Heat is lost during the compression stroke, thus reducing the value of T immediately before expansion.

(c) The heat is not added instantaneously at t.d.c., but the mixture begins to burn before t.d.c. and continues to do so for some part of the expansion stroke. As the pressure is dropping all the way on this stroke, it follows that the fuel burnt at the lower pressures will not be used to its fullest advantage.

(d) In order completely to discharge the burnt gases after expansion, it is necessary to open the exhaust valve a long way before b.d.c. of the stroke, and while there is still appreciable pressure in the cylinder. Thus, the effective expansion ratio is in practice always less than the compression ratio, as the effective stroke ends when the exhaust valve opens.

If the above are compared with the assumptions which have to be made in calculating the a.s.e. (see page 21), they certainly seem to represent formidable sources of loss of energy. Nevertheless, it is possible on a well-designed engine to obtain a thermal efficiency, in terms of ft.-lb. on the pistons, of 38 per cent. using a comp. r. of 7 : 1. The corresponding a.s.e. is 54 per cent., so that the result obtained is only 30 per cent. less than the theoretical ideal.

Calculating thermal efficiency

A simple example will make clear the requirements for calculating thermal efficiency in practice.

We have an engine which develops 30 b.h.p. steadily on test for a period of 1 hour, during which time it consumes 17 lb. of petrol which is known to have a calorific value of 18,000 B.Th.U. per lb. The thermal efficiency is required.

Reducing both " input " and " output " to a common quantity (B.Th.U.), we get:

Fuel consumed = 17 lb. Heat consumed = $17 \times 18,000 =$ 286,000 B.Th.U.

B.h.p. developed = 30. Time = 60 min. = $30 \times 60 \times 33,000$ ft.-lb. per hour.

As 1 B.Th.U. = 778 ft.-lb., heat available as work at crank-shaft =

$$\frac{30 \times 60 \times 33,000}{778} = 76,350 \text{ B.Th.U.}$$

Thus, brake thermal efficiency $= \dfrac{76,350}{286,000} = 26.7$ per cent.

As already mentioned, it is usual to include volumetric efficiency in the overall thermal efficiency, but if required the former can be measured separately. This might well be desirable when valve gear modifications or port design are concerned. Connection of the air intake to an accurate measuring device, such as a type of gasholder, would enable the volume inhaled to be measured over any required number of induction strokes, and comparison with the theoretical swept volume of the engine then gives the percentage volumetric efficiency. Obviously the volumetric efficiency will not remain constant in a variable-speed engine, since the valve timing must necessarily be a compromise, likewise the port area, factors which will be discussed later. A volumetric efficiency of around 80 per cent. is, however, obtainable on a good engine with overhead valves, over most of the useful speed range.

The mechanical efficiency can be measured, if required, on the dynamometer, by running the engine, at the same speed at which maximum b.h.p. is developed, with each of its cylinders cut out in turn. The reduction in b.h.p. under these conditions represents the i.h.p. of the cylinder cut out, and by adding all the " debits " together, the total i.h.p. can be obtained, and thus the mechanical efficiency (see page 24). The figure for this is again not constant, being less at the higher r.p.m. due to greater friction. It is usually above 80 per cent., and particular attention to free running of components may be rewarded by a figure approaching 88 per cent.

CHAPTER 2

The Production of Power

B.m.e.p. and torque—Power production—Compression ratio and detonation —Pressure increase with compression ratio—Heat loss—Water temperature— Valve size and gas velocity

B.m.e.p. and torque

The torque, or turning effort on the crankshaft, is naturally independent of engine speed, its value depending on the pressure on the pistons, their area, and the stroke. Since the dimensions of bore and stroke are fixed, it follows that any increase in m.e.p. means an increase in torque, and vice versa. Thus, m.e.p. and torque curves follow the same line on the performance graph.

As already stated, i.m.e.p. is obtained directly from indicator measurement of cylinder expansion pressure. On the test bed it is usual to calculate the pressure from the b.h.p. and refer to it as brake m.e.p., or b.m.e.p. The figure thus obtained is less than the i.m.e.p., as the mechanical losses are involved.

Knowing the b.h.p., the b.m.e.p. can be calculated as follows:

If $l =$ length of stroke in feet.

$a =$ area of one piston in sq. in.

$n =$ number of power strokes per min.

$$\text{B.m.e.p. (lb. per sq. in.)} = \frac{\text{b.h.p.} \times 33{,}000}{l \times a \times n}$$

The " make-up " of the above formula will be apparent if it is compared with the i.h.p. calculation on page 23.

To obtain the torque from the b.m.e.p., we can use a constant, since, for any engine, the only two variables affecting torque are the swept volume and the b.m.e.p., and all other mathematical calculations can be resolved into the constant, viz.:—

$$\text{Torque (lb. ft.)} = \frac{\text{b.m.e.p.} \times \text{swept volume in c.c.}}{2{,}473}$$

27

Power production

It will be apparent that if the torque of the engine remains constant, the b.h.p. will increase in direct proportion to the speed, and that the only limitation on power will be the mechanical construction of the engine in its ability to withstand high r.p.m. As a matter of fact, the mechanical construction in general does determine the limit, but this is accompanied by a falling off in torque due to the decreased b.m.e.p. and increased frictional losses.

The b.m.e.p. falls off as the revolutions increase because of the inability of the engine to inhale a full charge in the time available. Thus, while the torque curve is reasonably flat, the b.h.p. curve will climb approximately *pro rata* with the r.p.m. As the b.m.e.p. and torque falls off, the b.h.p. curve will begin to droop, and will flatten out in turn, until a point is reached when more r.p.m. does not produce any more power. The mechanical limitations at top revolutions mainly concern the stresses arising from inertia of the reciprocating parts, notably, of course, the pistons. As has been shown, high piston speeds make for high thermal efficiency (in itself an aid to good torque), but the mechanical limit has to be considered.

The b.m.e.p. obtainable is very considerably influenced by the compression ratio, as is obvious from a consideration of the fundamental principles governing the air standard efficiency. There are, however, limiting factors. These are, that a very high comp. r. may necessitate a shape of combustion chamber which is not conducive to high thermal efficiency, due to the requirement of providing as small a volume as possible; and secondly, the liability of detonation of the charge. This latter point will be considered next.

Compression ratio and detonation

Research carried out by eminent engineers, notably Ricardo, over a long period, have shown that detonation, or " knocking," arises from the production in the combustion chamber of an explosion wave, due to rapid ignition and combustion of a portion of the charge. On expanding, this portion compresses the unburnt part of the charge, which in turn rapidly increases in temperature until it ignites uncontrollably and nearly instantaneously. The shock wave set up gives rise to a characteristic metallic sound, and can vary in magnitude between a mild form, occurring only at relatively low speeds and wide throttle openings (popularly known as "pinking") to such violent manifestations that the engine pulls up dead.

The choice of fuel has a decisive influence on detonation, inferior fuels demanding comparatively low compression ratios if the combustion process is to take place as desired. Modern high-grade fuels allow of high ratios being used with the expansion process under complete control, whilst, of course, special mixtures for purely racing purposes allow of ratios so high that the limit thereon is set by mechanical considerations inside the cylinder head.

Fuel technology is a formidable subject in itself, and hardly within the scope of this book. However, it will be useful to mention one aspect, namely, the grading of fuel by what is known as the octane number. Generally speaking, the higher the octane number the better the quality of the fuel, and the higher the comp. r. that can be used without detonation.

In obtaining the octane rating, a compound called iso-octane is added to the fuel to diminish the tendency to detonation. The fuel is then tested on a variable-compression engine in the laboratory, so that a performance is obtained just free from detonation. The fuel is graded by an octane number equivalent to the percentage of iso-octane in it; for example, a mixture of 80 per cent. iso-octane and 20 per cent. heptane (one of which decreases, and the other of which increases, the tendency to detonate) would be known as 80-octane fuel. Any other fuel which could be used successfully in the test engine under the same conditions would also be 80-octane rated, quite irrespective of its ingredients. Its number would mean that it possesses the same anti-detonation properties as fuel containing the appropriate proportions of iso-octane and heptane.

The late-lamented "pool" petrol had an octane rating of about 72, while the normally obtainable high-grade brands

are 80-octane, a rating which is generally suitable for normal
requirements on sports-type engines.

It is important to note that the calorific value of high-
octane fuel may be inferior to that of more ordinary petrols.
The latter have a calorific value of about 18,000 B.Th.U. per
lb., whereas the same weight of a high-octane racing fuel may
well produce only about half this figure, so that a very much

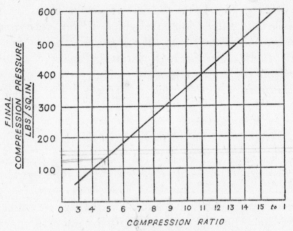

Increase of final pressure with compression ratio
(before ignition).

greater quantity of fuel is required to produce the same
amount of heat. This, of course, explains the abnormal
increase in size of carburetter components, pipe-lines and so
on, required when such fuels are used. The much higher
thermal efficiency obtainable naturally results in a nett power
gain, whilst the high latent heat of evaporation assists in
lowering internal temperatures; a good point so long as the
fuel is not used deliberately to this end.

Pressure increase with compression ratio

The object of increasing the comp. r. is obviously to increase
the torque. Particularly when really extensive increases in
power output are contemplated, it is necessary to know what
is involved in so doing. If, for example, a 50 per cent. increase

in b.h.p. is contemplated, and the maximum r.p.m. remains much the same, this means a 50 per cent. increase in b.m.e.p. or an increase, say, from 100 lb. per sq. in. to 150.

The graph showing cylinder pressures at various compression ratios (page 30) is instructive. It should be noted that the pressure indicated is that at the end of the compression stroke, and assumes adequate cylinder filling, i.e., good volumetric efficiency. At the moment of ignition the pressure will rise to a maximum of three or four times the compression pressure. Graph (page 32) shows approximate b.h.p. figures obtained on engines of similar construction, using firstly, 72-octane petrol, and secondly, an alcohol-base fuel allowing 12 : 1 comp. r.

The final compression pressure is, as mentioned before, governed largely by the volumetric efficiency. Assuming induction at atmospheric pressure, and $\gamma = 1.3$

$$\text{Final comp. pressure} = 14.7 \times r^{1.3}$$

In practice, of course, induction will not be at atmospheric pressure, but somewhat lower, so that any pressure calculated as above will be on the " safe " side.

When an engine has been modified to the extent of even a moderate increase in torque, it is very necessary that detonation is not allowed. What would be innocuous pinking on a lower comp. r. can have serious results if judged by the same degree of audibility, and permitted on higher ratios. It is usually the case that, on a particular fuel, a comp. r. on which the engine is perfectly happy, is only fractionally lower than the one at which all kinds of troubles may intervene, and the latter ratio gives but negligible increase in power.

The noise of detonation in a high-compression engine using the correct grade of fuel is much less easy to detect than on a less thermally efficient engine burning low-octane petrol, so that it is essential to look for other more reliable evidence that, after modification, the engine is free from detonation.

Heat loss

In comparing the average thermal efficiency figure with a.s.e. for equivalent comp. r., it is evident that even in the very best designs a good proportion of the fuel energy goes to waste. We have already indicated some of the reasons for a possible 30 per cent. discrepancy between actual and a.s.e. figures, and one important point mentioned was the inevitable early opening of the exhaust valve. This, as will be shown, accounts for most of the loss.

Assuming an indicated thermal efficiency of 35 per cent., this means a loss of 65 per cent., and of this we can expect

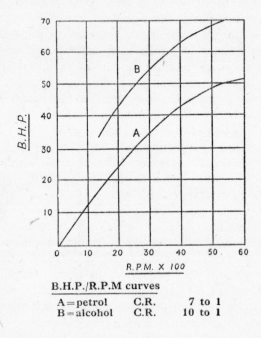

B.H.P./R.P.M curves

A = petrol	C.R.	7 to 1
B = alcohol	C.R.	10 to 1

nearly 40 per cent. to go to exhaust. The remaining 25 per cent. is carried away in the cooling water.

The heat loss to the cylinders, and thus to the cooling water, takes place roughly as 5 per cent. during initial combustion, 6 per cent. during expansion, and the remaining 14 per cent. during exhaust. Of this last-named loss, none can possibly be recovered, so we are left with 11 per cent. to be accounted for during the combustion and expansion processes.

Obviously, the combustion-expansion strokes, even with no heat loss at all, could never be 100 per cent. efficient.

The efficiency of the processes depends on the compression ratio, and is governed by thermodynamic laws. It can safely be said that the ignition process accounts for a loss of 5 out of the 11 per cent. mentioned, and that the process in itself must lose half of this, the jacket loss therefore accounting for $2\frac{1}{2}$ per cent. As for expansion, it might be thought that as the cylinder wall is uncovered by the descending piston, a serious heat loss could take place due to the large area of metal exposed. It should be borne in mind, however, that the pressure is dropping all the time, and thus heat loss towards the end of expansion is not so serious, since in any case its retention would have added little to the work done before the exhaust valve opened. In fact it is doubtful if, of the 6 per cent. lost during expansion, more than one-fifth could be saved even with no jacket loss whatever. Thus, the total saving amounting to 3.7 per cent., would be very small even if all the heat could be trapped. This represents a gain in thermal efficiency from 35 to 38.7 per cent. Actually the gain would be less, as due to the higher operating temperature of the mixture, and its consequent increase in specific heat, there would be a decrease in thermal efficiency from this cause, so that the nett gain would probably only be about 2 per cent.

The significance of the above lies in the fact that high thermal efficiencies are sometimes claimed for engines on the basis of the use of a compact form of combustion chamber, the idea being that such a shape presents the minimum area for loss of heat to the cooling jackets. It is obvious that this cannot be so, and the probability is that the high thermal efficiency figures obtained by such engines are due almost solely to the good " breathing " characteristics which usually go with a compact head shape.

Water temperature

It is, of course, a fact that engines run better when the cooling water is hot, and the reason frequently given is that the increased temperature leads to higher pressures and less heat loss. Actually, the improvement in running when hot is almost entirely due to the improved carburation and mixture distribution afforded by the warm induction arrangements,

C

and to the decreased piston friction and improved ring sealing which is a result of the thinning of the oil on the bores.

As the weight of mixture inhaled into the cylinders is proportionate to its absolute temperature, it is obvious that with cool cylinders a greater weight of charge will be drawn in than when the temperature is higher. This will more than compensate for any increase in heat loss to the cool jackets, and as far as the i.h.p. is concerned, there will be a definite gain. However, the extra piston oil-drag with cold oil cancels out this gain, so that the b.h.p. figure will be lower when the engine is cold, the decreased mechanical efficiency more than compensating for the increased volumetric efficiency.

In showing that, with all combustion and expansion heat losses completely cancelled (if this were possible) the gain in thermal efficiency would be extremely small, we have considered an engine which is already thermally efficient, i.e., a figure of 35 per cent. was chosen. Actually, there are many engines which do not operate at anything like this figure, though by dint of extravagant fuel consumption they can be made to perform reasonably well.

It should be remembered, however, that performance obtained in this way is objectionable not merely because of waste of fuel, but for a far more important reason. For the engine to be efficient, in every meaning of the word, it must burn its fuel to the utmost possible advantage from the point of view of power production. If as big a percentage as possible of the heat energy is converted to work on the pistons, good design will take care of the disposal of the remainder which is unavoidably wasted. If the percentage converted to work is reduced, a greater proportion has to be got away to waste, and that extra can spell trouble in the course of long periods of full-load operation.

Valve size and gas velocity

The dimensions of valves and ports have necessarily to be something of a compromise. For the desirable amount of turbulence, to prevent stagnant areas of mixture, in particular adjacent to the cylinder walls, high gas speed through the inlet valve is required. On the other hand, an excessive gas speed means reduced volumetric efficiency and increased pumping work.

In general, it may be said that reasonably high gas velocity is the most important consideration. If this sets up a degree of turbulence which adequately scours the walls, combustion and expansion heat losses will be minimized, combustion will be complete, and m.e.p. satisfactorily high. In the type of engine with which we are mainly concerned, with overhead valves, the volumetric efficiency should not suffer, in view of the very free entry afforded for the gas. Whilst therefore it is desirable to reduce pumping work to the minimum, increasing of port areas and valve sizes should not be done haphazardly, particularly if by so doing the shape of the combustion chamber is altered, since turbulence obviously depends largely on the compactness of the latter.

As far as the exhaust valve is concerned, it should cause little concern in regard to power loss. The relatively early opening, when there is still a high pressure (in the neighbourhood of 70 lb. per sq. in. above atm.) in the cylinder, ensures a rapid exit of spent gas, so that the energy required to pump out the residue is negligible. Most of the gas is expelled when the piston is around b.d.c., so that the back pressure on the exhaust up-stroke will not exceed 1 or 2 lb. per sq. in., and, in view of the kinetic energy of the escaping gas column, will be considerably less at high speeds, unless the silencer and exhaust pipe are outrageously inefficient.

Thus, while it is found that an inlet gas velocity above about 160 lb. per sq. in. is liable to lead to an increase in the pumping losses and a decrease in the weight of charge drawn in, the velocity through the exhaust valve may be up to 50 per cent. higher than this before any measurable back pressure occurs. Even if the back pressure is doubled, say from 1 to 2 lb. per sq. in., this only decreases the m.e.p. by a like amount. A negative inlet pressure of 2 lb., on the other hand, represents a reduction from 14.7 to 12.7 lb. per sq. in., or about 14 per cent.—a much more serious matter, as it reduces the m.e.p. by approximately the same percentage.

Chapter 3

Problems of Cylinder Charging

Valve timing—Maximum charging—Overlap snags—High-speed operation—
Pulsating pressure—High power; narrow speed range—
Application to multi-cylinder engines—Exhaust systems

Valve timing

As has been seen in Chapter 1, when calculating the
theoretical thermal efficiency of an engine having a certain
compression ratio, various assumptions are made. Amongst
these are, that each stroke occupies 180 deg., and that the
induction and exhaust strokes take place at atmospheric
pressure. In practice, of course, even on wide throttle and
at maximum torque, with the engine turning over at perhaps
half its peak r.p.m., when there is plenty of time for the
mixture to fill the cylinders, we know that the induction
pressure will be barely equal to atmospheric. As regards the
exhaust stroke, this commences when there is still a high
pressure in the cylinder, and a proportion of mixture representing useful power is forcibly ejected to waste.

In practice also, the valve timing is arranged so that the
inlet valve, instead of closing at b.d.c., remains open for a
considerable portion of the following compression stroke, while
the exhaust valve remains open after t.d.c. of the exhaust
stroke, the inlet valve being open at the same time, this feature
representing the " overlap " period between the two valves.

The object of such valve timing is, of course, to take
advantage of the inertia of the gas columns to assist in filling
the cylinders. If the inlet valve opens at t.d.c. the piston will
be well down the induction stroke before the mixture in the
inlet port and pipe begin to move ; thus the valve is usually
timed to open earlier so that it is fully open when the piston
begins to descend. At b.d.c. the piston stops momentarily,
but the rapidly moving gas column does not, since it is not
only attempting to catch up on the slightly lower pressure
inside the cylinder (compared with atmospheric), but is now

possessed of considerable momentum which continues to propel it into the cylinder, and will do so even when the piston begins to rise on the compression stroke. Not until there is danger of reversal of gas flow back through the inlet valve, is the latter closed, and this may be 50 deg. or more after b.d.c.

Maximum charging

When the exhaust valve timing is examined we may find, as already mentioned, the valve opening perhaps 50 deg. or so before b.d.c. of the expansion stroke. This apparent wastage of expansion pressure, and a useful portion of the stroke, is unavoidable, because if the valve opening is delayed there simply is not time to expel the burnt charge. The task of doing this would devolve on the piston, on its upward exhaust stroke. This would be unacceptable, since the negative work involved mechanically in expelling the exhaust would entail a loss far greater than any gain made by continuing the expansion stroke for a longer period.

At t.d.c. of the exhaust stroke it will be noted that the inlet valve has just opened. The high-speed exit of spent gases through the exhaust valve has, however, been continuing for some time, so that there is negligible pressure existing in the cylinder, and no tendency for an exhaust back-flow into the inlet port. In fact, the designer relies on the momentum of the exhaust gas column to clear the waste products from the cylinder head. Obviously there is no other way of scavenging the combustion chamber, as this is unswept mechanically by the piston. To this end, then, the exhaust valve is kept open for some 20 deg. after t.d.c., when the piston is accelerating on the induction stroke. As the inlet valve is fully open, the tendency for the exhaust gas column to reverse back into the cylinder is not very marked on a wide throttle, unless the closing of the valve is delayed. It will be evident, however, these such reversals, in both inlet and exhaust passages, can conceivably take place at certain combinations of throttle opening and engine speed.

The valve timing has thus to be very much of a compromise, and the more flexible the engine, the less liberties can be taken with extended opening periods and overlap (when both

valves are open together at t.d.c. of the exhaust stroke). It
is quite usual on engine tests to find exhaust residuals left in
the combustion chambers, in varying amounts as between
cylinders, at certain loads, even when the valve timing is
such as to promote good scavenging. On the other hand,
traces of fresh mixture can many times be detected in the
exhaust outlet, showing that the scavenge is effectively
preventing the fresh charge from going its proper way into the

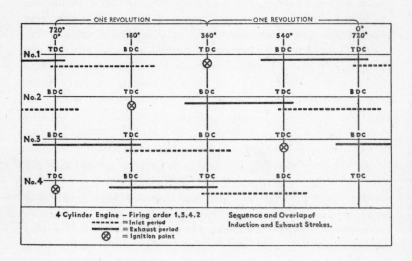

4 Cylinder Engine – Firing order 1,3,4,2
- - - - - = Inlet period
————— = Exhaust period
⊗ = Ignition point

Sequence and Overlap of
Induction and Exhaust Strokes.

cylinder. Such faults certainly show up, as a rule, only at
reduced throttle openings, and this may account for the fact
that fuel economy on light loads is in many cases not so marked
as might be expected.

It will be evident that on small throttle openings the whole
induction system will be operating at a pressure very much
below atmospheric. Under such conditions, assuming normal
valve timing, three of the inlet valves in a four-cylinder engine
will open during any half-revolution. As an example, we
can consider the valve as timed to open 10 deg. before t.d.c.
and to close 60 deg. after b.d.c. Thus, with the piston of
No. 1 cylinder starting on its induction stroke, its inlet valve
will be about fully open. However, the inlet valve on No. 2
cylinder, whose piston is starting from b.d.c. of its compression

stroke, will still be open and will remain so for a further 60 deg. Finally, the inlet valve of No. 3 cylinder (which is exhausting) will open just as this piston arrives at t.d.c. Going back to No. 1 again, this inlet valve will still be fully open as it arrives at b.d.c. A study of the diagram on page 38 will make this clear.

Overlap snags

Now consider what happens in the running conditions described above. The exhaust valve of No. 1 is still open and the residual gases are flowing out, when its inlet valve opens. At low speeds, and with little weight of mixture, the out-flowing exhaust will have little inertia effect and thus the opening of the inlet valve against the low pressure existing in the induction pipe is quite likely to draw the exhaust back into the cylinder momentarily. In the case of No. 2, only the inlet valve is open, so there can be no dilution of mixture, but a reversal of flow in the inlet port may take place, depending on the balance of induction and compression pressures in the cylinder. As for No. 3, very much the same conditions apply as for No. 1, that is, danger of contamination with exhaust residuals.

Thus, with early inlet valve opening, some loss of power must be accepted at light throttle opening and medium speed, and idling may be unavoidably irregular, since under these conditions induction vacuum is at its maximum. It would therefore appear that the more flexibility we want from the engine, the less able we are to take advantage of gas momentum. This is true, but it is quite feasible to arrive at a compromise which gives a good torque over a useful speed range, and is perfectly satisfactory for all normal purposes. It is when considering sports and racing-type engines that the possibility of using " pipe energy " becomes most attractive. Such engines can be expected to be driven regularly on wide throttle, so that the pressure in the induction pipe more nearly approaches atmospheric, and there is a greater weight of mixture inhaled to form a high-speed " bung " travelling down the exhaust pipe. In such conditions, the valve timing and overlap period can be arranged to induce the maximum amount of charge to enter the cylinders under given conditions of throttle opening and speed, but it must be appreciated that for any real effect, the throttle opening must be generous, the useful engine speed of limited range, and the piston speed high enough to obtain the requisite gas speed through the ports.

High-speed operation

It will be useful to take an example of a sports engine designed to take advantage of gas momentum. Its inlet valve may open 40 deg. before t.d.c., and close 80 deg. after b.d.c.—a generous opening period of 300 deg. The exhaust timing will be similar to that of the inlet, closing 40 deg. after t.d.c. and opening 80 deg. before b.d.c., resulting in an overlap of 80 deg. at exhaust t.d.c.

Starting with the exhaust valve, this opens early, the expansion stroke being of only 100 deg. duration. This means that the cylinder pressure is still high at the time of valve opening, and the gas escapes with considerable energy, the bulk of it getting away before b.d.c. when the piston is travelling slowly. As the piston accelerates on the exhaust stroke, it probably just about catches up with the remaining gas, until, when the piston has passed its peak speed and is slowing due to crank angularity, the cylinder pressure is becoming sub-atmospheric because of the momentum of the exhaust gases in the outlet pipe, coupled with the decrease of piston speed. At this point, the inlet valve opens, and the cylinder head is charged with fresh mixture by exhaust extractor action alone. After t.d.c., the piston descends on the induction stroke, but, since the exhaust valve is still open for another 40 deg., both piston and exhaust outflow combine not only to inhale the maximum weight of charge, but also to maintain the gas speed necessary for turbulence through what must be a relatively large inlet valve and port. As a result, the weight of inlet charge builds up its own momentum, so that at b.d.c. it still continues to flow in, against the back pressure of the rising piston, for 80 deg. of the compression stroke, until the piston speed approaches its peak. At this point, when there is danger of gas-flow reversal, the inlet valve is closed.

It will be accepted that while the foregoing method of inducing a weighty inlet charge is excellent from the point of view of sheer torque at high r.p.m., it might be expected to be somewhat extravagant as there would seem to be grave danger of a good deal of charge loss down the exhaust pipe, particularly during the early opening inlet valve phase, when the piston is still ascending. It is, in fact, remarkable how thermally efficient engines designed on such lines can be made, the figures standing more than favourable comparison with the best types of touring engines. Much of this is due to very careful port design. If the direction of flow of the inlet gas is taken care of, little loss of charge need take place. It will be obvious that although the valve opening periods and overlap seem large, the time intervals at high speeds are short, and as the charge weight increases, so does its inertia.

In considering the effects obtained from taking advantage of the rapid movement of inlet and exhaust gas columns, we have so far visualized what might be described as " bungs " of gas acting somewhat after the manner of auxiliary pistons. As far as a straightforward explanation goes, this is satisfactory, but in practice the actual behaviour of the gas is not quite so simple.

Pulsating pressure

The gas flow, far from proceeding smoothly, actually takes the form of a series of pulsations, or pressure waves, alternating as positive and negative pressures above and below the mean. This is, of course, in accordance with physical laws that have been known for many years, and are made use of in wind instruments. The pulsations in engine pipework can be both helpful and a nuisance; they are much less likely to become the latter if miraculous effects are not expected from them in the first place.

Due to its length of pipe, high initial pressure, and relatively uncomplicated layout, the exhaust system lends itself most readily to harnessing this pulsating pressure, though the phenomenon should not be lost sight of in designing inlet pipes. The frequency of the pulsations depends largely on the exhaust pipe length and its diameter, and, to a lesser extent, on engine speed. High engine speed tends to reduce the negative pressure waves, with less liability to upset the inlet gas flow in cases where considerable overlap is used to augment this. It will, of course, be evident that if the exhaust pipe dimensions are laid out for a definite valve timing and engine speed, power output at other speeds may be seriously affected.

However, to take an outstanding example of what can be done by scientifically harnessing the pulsating pressure, we need look no further than the typical British 500 c.c. single-cylinder racing engine. The pipework on such an engine is simplicity itself, comprising merely a short intake stub from carburetter to inlet port, and an exhaust pipe of suitable length and varying diameter as called for. It has already been explained how, with a high-speed exhaust gas exit and a lengthy overlap period, the cylinder head can be scavenged of residuals and charged with fresh mixture while the piston is still descending on the exhaust stroke. The power obtained from the modern racing 500 is, however, such that there is much more to it than good scavenging; something in fact that amounts quite literally to a supercharge.

It has been mentioned that charge loss down the exhaust pipe is liable to take place if the exhaust valve closing is delayed unduly on the inlet stroke. In the case of the sports engine previously quoted, the exhaust valve closed 40 deg. after t.d.c. Now, imagine that, by utilizing very high gas velocity in the first place, and a correct design of open pipe for the specified conditions of engine speed and throttle opening, we can continue to draw a fresh inlet charge down the exhaust pipe even when the piston is approaching its maximum speed on the inlet stroke. We are now obtaining a cylinder filling rapidly with mixture, plus a further volume of fresh mixture in the exhaust pipe, between, as it were, the exhaust " bung " and the exhaust valve.

It would seem that all that is going to happen is that good mixture will be sent to waste. But supposing we can induce the exhaust pressure wave to reverse at the right moment. The extra inlet charge in the exhaust pipe will be pushed back into the cylinder through the exhaust valve, and added to the charge already flowing in through the inlet valve (the velocity of which flow will prevent its reversal). As soon as there is danger of exhaust residuals following the inlet charge into the combustion chamber, the exhaust valve is closed, and we are left with what amounts to a supercharged cylinder, quite free, without benefit of blower.

High power; narrow speed range

One of the most successful examples of the application of the above theory developing in pre-war years just under 50 b.h.p. at 6,700 r.p.m. from its single 499 c.c. cylinder, had an inlet period of 320 deg., an exhaust period of 325 deg., and an overlap of 125 deg. The fantastic nature of these figures is best illustrated by considering that in the 720 deg. constituting the engine cycle, there is a period of only 200 deg. during which no valve is open, and in this period, both compression and expansion strokes take place. The latest examples of these engines peak at considerably over 7,000 r.p.m. and there is little doubt that an increase in b.h.p. has been obtained just about *pro rata* to the increase in revolutions.

Obviously, if not only gas velocity but pressure waves are to be taken advantage of in the search for power, there are so many factors involved that an absolutely minimum engine speed range becomes of paramount importance. Ideally, the designer should be able to concentrate on arranging components to suit a constant-speed power unit with a fixed throttle opening. In practice, cynics may aver that some engines behave very much as if this ideal had been realized.

The exhaust pipe effect is influenced not only by its dimensions, i.e., diameter and length, but also by the shape of outlet. The frequency of the pressure pulsations can be altered by the use of a trumpet-shaped exit, and experiment in this direction may prove advantageous. The technique of pipe-end design is mainly a matter of trial and error, and there is little doubt that shapes other than a plain trumpet or megaphone may be evolved to greater effect. The latest efforts are in the direction of using a divergent-convergent shape (or " reverse-cone ") which is claimed to increase the speed range over which the supercharge takes place.

With regard to the inlet pipe, again referring to the single-cylinder, the main object here is to obtain sufficient gas velocity to allow the pressure to build up in the cylinder without causing a flow reversal in the inlet port. Normally, the closer the carburetter is to the inlet valve, the better, and in cases of doubt, this is a cast-iron rule. It may, however, be possible to obtain a slight increase of power, providing the exhaust pipe is correct, by extending the intake length between valve and carburetter choke, when the augmented inlet velocity will allow the exhaust valve closing time to be further delayed. Obviously, this extra length of inlet ducting will contain fuel-air mixture, and it can be assumed that at the gas speeds and temperatures involved the additional piping will not induce too much precipitation of fuel on the pipe walls. The use of a long air-intake pipe between the atmosphere and the carburetter choke is of doubtful utility except in so far as it helps to obtain an eddy-free air flow to the jet. Any idea that the air column itself has any self-charging effect is a fallacy; in fact, the extra flow friction is likely to hamper rather than help.

Application to multi-cylinder engines

The considerable increase in maximum b.h.p. which has been obtained over the years from single-cylinder engines, as a result of harnessing the pipework, is something that has required a long period of time and much painstaking trial and error. It is not difficult to lay down a theory regarding what happens, and in fact a workable design, with suitable dimensions of inlet and exhaust tracts and piping, can be laid down from theoretical considerations, without too much trouble. The maximum benefit can, however, only be obtained by experiment. When one considers all the possible variations, not only in pipe size and diameter, but in valve and port area, piston speed, valve timing and lift, carburetter size, and so on, it will be appreciated that long hours on the test bed and much hard labour have gone into producing the results that are seen to the best advantage on the motor-cycle T.T. circuit in June. (See page 81.)

That being the case, it will be obvious that no magic result can be expected from removing the silencer from a standard engine and substituting a foreshortened exhaust pipe with a megaphone outlet, plus a larger carburetter jet. The same remark applies to thus equipping an engine designed for use with a plain parallel pipe.

In order to apply the single-cylinder technique to multi-cylinder units of the type with which we are more concerned, it is, of course, necessary to treat each cylinder individually, particularly as far as the inlet side is concerned. This means a separate carburetter and inlet port for each cylinder. With such an arrangement, each inlet tract is direct to the valve and variations in length for experimental purposes are readily accommodated. It will be evident, however, that although some advantage may be gained by increasing the inlet charge momentum so as to allow the closing of the inlet valve to be delayed somewhat longer than normally after the start of the compression stroke, the fullest use cannot be obtained unless the exhaust side is also involved.

The normal sports engine, except in semi-racing form, does not go to the complication and expense of one carburetter per cylinder. It is usual for this type of engine to have one carburetter serving two cylinders of a " four " or three cylinders of a " six," though first-class examples of the latter are also fitted with three carburetters. It is possible to so arrange the inlet manifolding that equally spaced aspiration periods are obtained on a four-cylinder, but as this means that one pipe must connect cylinders 1 and 4, and another pipe cylinders 2 and 3, it will be obvious that the layout will involve some awkward lengths and bends which encourage fuel deposition and increase gas friction. For this reason it is usual to feed adjacent cylinders (1–2 and 3–4) from the two carburetters, even though the aspiration periods are uneven.

In the case of a six-cylinder equal aspiration periods are obtained by feeding adjacent cylinders (1–2–3 and 4–5–6) from the two carburetters, so that the layout is excellent both from this standpoint and that of short and compact piping. Sixes with three carburetters (1–2, 3–4, 5–6) will have uneven aspiration periods, but may benefit from the shorter inlet tract.

Exhaust systems

For engines having individual carburetters to each cylinder, it would seem logical to use an entirely separate exhaust pipe per cylinder, so enabling the pipes to be tuned in line with single-cylinder technique. As far as normal layouts are concerned, the main requirement is to prevent interference between cylinders due to overlapping exhaust strokes, and to provide sufficient length in each exhaust branch to give a useful extractor effect before the separate pipes merge.

There may be some difficulty in accommodating a system having branch pipes of suitable length feeding a single tail-pipe, and division of the system is frequently resorted to in order to simplify matters. Thus, a four-cylinder engine, fitted with Y-branches from cylinders 1–4 and 2–3, the two branches then leading into a common tailpipe, would give equal time intervals in the exhaust expulsions with little or no possibility of backflow into the cylinders. Similarly, a six with two trifurcating branches for cylinders 1–2–3 and 4–5–6 would have a similar effect. Duplication of the complete tail-pipe system is occasionally met with, each branch in this case having its own pipe and silencer.

It has already been mentioned in Chapter 2 that due to the considerable pressure existing on the exhaust stroke, resistance to gas movement has much less disadvantageous effects than would be the case in regard to the induction system. This is the reason why many engines operate quite well with exhaust manifolding the design of which can be most charitably assumed to be due to foundry limitations or lack of room under the engine cover. The fact that certain sports engines can gain several b.h.p. by substitution of a " special " mani-folding and pipes is certainly no credit to the substitution, but merely a strong condemnation of the standard design.

CHAPTER 4

Mechanical Construction of High-Power Engines

*Basic materials in construction—Non-ferrous materials—Fatigue failure—
Valve operation—Twin o.h.c. engines—Single o.h.c. engines—Crankshafts
—Bearings and materials*

Basic materials in construction

The first requirement for ensuring reliability under conditions of continuous high-speed operation, is that the materials chosen shall be of the correct type, and adequate for the duty, of any particular task. The advances made in foundry and metallurgical technique of recent years have ensured that under normal conditions, failure of a component is comparatively rare. It is still possible, of course, to encounter cases of fracture of such items as connecting rods or crankshafts under abnormal stresses, as in racing, but these can arise from many other causes than faulty material or dimensional errors.

There are two main classes of materials used in engine construction—ferrous and non-ferrous. The former comprise those with an iron base, such as cast-iron, mild steel, and alloy steel. The last-named can be case-hardened or otherwise specially treated as required for particular duties. A fairly recent newcomer to the ferrous range is high-duty or high-tensile iron, in which various compounds are mixed to achieve a high degree of toughness and strength. This material is coming to the fore as an alternative to steel for crankshafts, Meehanite being a typical and familiar name in this connection.

Present-day foundry technique allows castings to be manufactured, the intricacy of which was unknown twenty years ago. This allows several " units " to be embodied in the same casting, which is all to the good from the point of view of rigidity and strength, though perhaps less desirable from the angle of accessibility when overhauls are contemplated. For instance, it is the custom nowadays to make the cylinder block, crankcase, and main bearing scantlings in one piece, with the cylinder head detachable above the top of the swept bore. This undoubtedly makes for a more accurately aligned and rigid assembly than the use of a separate crankcase with detachable cylinder block. The latter, on the other hand, when combined with its head, had many virtues, notably in the absence of a complicated gas-and-water joint with its attendant studs, bosses and sealing gasket.

Non-ferrous materials

Aluminium alloy is, of course, the most used of the non-ferrous range. It combines adequate strength with lightness, and is on the whole easier to cast and machine than iron. Its high thermal conductivity is also a very desirable feature in certain applications.

For large castings carrying little stress, ordinary cast aluminium is excellent. Thus it is widely used for oil-containers, valve and timing gear covers, and so on. As far as oil-containers are concerned, the virtues of aluminium from the point of view of heat conductivity in comparison with, say, a pressed steel sump, are probably over-rated, since oil temperature should be kept within bounds by other aspects of design. However, the aluminium sump does combine strength with lightness, and this is a requirement in sumps of large capacity which are a " must " for high-efficiency engines.

The thermal conductivity of aluminium really shows to advantage in the use of the material for cylinder heads. It will be apparent from a study of the theory of the operating cycle, that the temperature range of the cycle has an important bearing on thermal efficiency, and that, whilst rapid heat dissipation at certain high-temperature phases in the cycle is essential to prevent overheating, retention of heat at other phases is desirable. Thus, a material which will rapidly transfer the heat between the mixture and the cooling water, in whichever direction is required, will make for high thermal efficiency as well as reliability under sustained high loading. A material of lower thermal conductivity characteristics, on the other hand, will tend to retain the heat within itself,

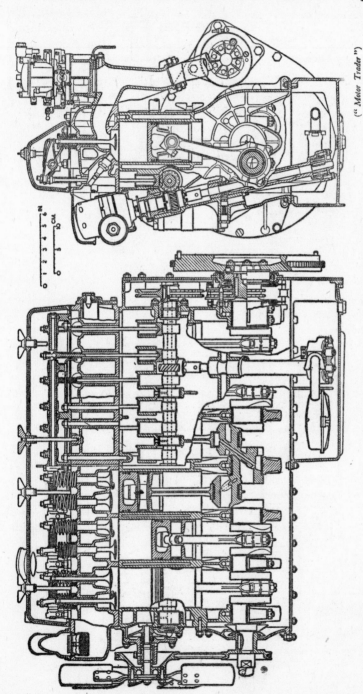

("Motor Trader")

THE 3-LITRE ALVIS WHICH IS USED IN A HEALEY MODEL

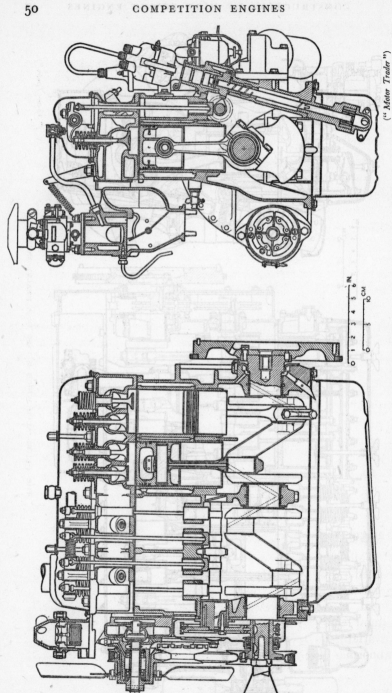

("Motor Trader")

THE STANDARD VANGUARD WHICH POWERS THE PLUS FOUR MORGAN OF 2,088 C.C.

leading to local superheated areas in conditions of high-temperature operation. For very high pressures, heads of aluminium-bronze alloy are sometimes used, as the mechanical strength in this case is equal to that of cast-iron, and valve-seat inserts (required with aluminium heads) may be dispensed with. Barronia metal, a copper-tin base alloy, is another successful material which can be used without valve-seat inserts.

Light-alloy crankcases, at one time common when separate cylinder blocks were the rule, are found occasionally, in which case the casting also incorporates the water-jacket, special iron cylinder liners being used. These are usually of the wet type, seating on suitable sealing rings at top and bottom to form a water joint with the aluminium casting. This form of construction makes for a commendably light power unit, but inevitably involves more machining operations and greater cost than the simple iron casting containing the bores therein.

Aluminium alloy is used without exception for pistons, usually in die-cast form, though forged pistons may be preferable for very high-speed work. The metal is chosen as much for its heat-conducting properties as for its lightness, since for adequate strength, the pistons are sufficiently robust in section to have considerable weight. No other metal would, however, be suitable, as ultra-rapid heat conduction from the piston crown to the cylinder walls is of outstanding importance.

Connecting rods have at times been made of duralumin or similar alloys, but forged steel is generally favoured, while as far as crankshafts are concerned, steel is still mostly used, though high-duty iron, notably Meehanite, has recently come to the fore, with cast construction instead of the usual forging.

Fatigue failure

Failure of highly stressed parts was at one time frequently caused by an actual fault in the metal—a " flaw," as it was popularly termed. Nowadays, such failures are very exceptional, modern methods of production and inspection being almost foolproof. Breakages in modern engines almost invariably arise from fatigue, or tiring of the metal under abnormal stresses, resulting in a crack developing. Once such a fracture has started, it will, of course, rapidly spread until complete breakage occurs. The greater the factor of safety in the component, the less liability there is to fatigue, but where reciprocating parts are concerned superfluous weight of metal is undesirable. Unfortunately, these parts are the very ones in which fractures are most serious and frequent. Old age also leads to changes in the metal structure which lessen its resistance to fatigue, a point to watch where "vintage" engines are under consideration. (See page 84.)

Elimination of places which are liable to encourage the start of cracks is an important part of correct design. Such places may be found at sudden changes of section, at the bottoms of screw-threads, junctions of bolt-heads with their shanks, and so on. Accidental scratches or file-marks can lead to early fracture, and, conversely, a high polish is a distinct discouragement to breakage. In this connection, it has been established by test that an accidental scratch on a polished surface causes a reduction in fatigue resistance of 15 per cent., while the finishing of a normal-smooth surface with fine carborundum to a high polish will result in an increase of 2 per cent.

Examination of a fracture can often provide useful information. The final breakage point is usually discernible by the rough portion at the break, the remaining part being almost polished in appearance, with curved lines which can often be traced back to their starting point. This semi-polished surface is caused by the working together of the surfaces before the final parting, and the start of the trouble is sometimes traceable to the commencement of the curved lines aforementioned. Investigation by an expert metallurgist can often give a clue to the direction of the force causing the breakage, and thus help in determining whether an abnormal load in the normal direction was responsible or whether some additional stress of an unlooked-for nature made its presence felt.

In very many respects the design of the competition car power unit follows closely its more sober counterpart. In fact, many of the components used on the latter types can be employed with equal success in engines of greater power out-

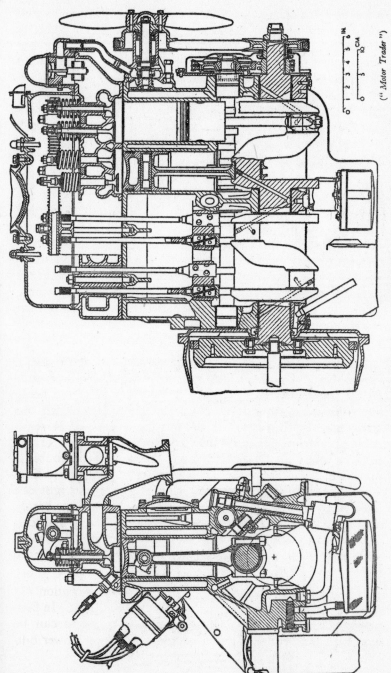

SECTION OF THE AUSTIN A90 ENGINE. A DUAL CARBURETTER VERSION POWERS THE AUSTIN-HEALEY "HUNDRED"

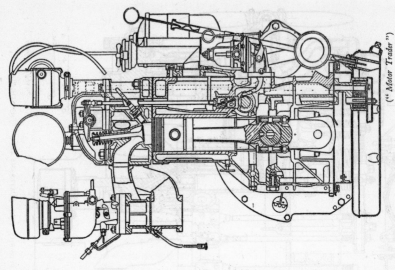

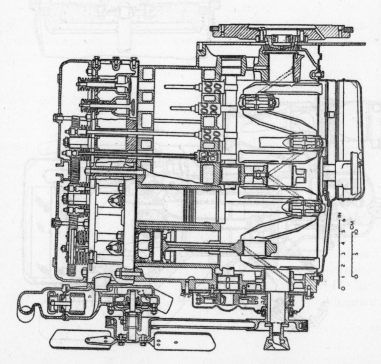

("Motor Trader")

AN "ALPINE" FAVOURITE—THE SUNBEAM-TALBOT 90

put, providing they can cope with the extra stresses involved. A study of the chapters dealing with specifications of typical engines will help to indicate how various manufacturers deal with particular aspects of design. Here, we will consider briefly some general points of particular interest.

Valve operation

The driving of crankcase-mounted camshafts, as used with side-valve and many o.h.v. layouts, is almost universally by roller chain. In cases where the shafts are only a little distance apart, a simple non-adjustable drive is sometimes employed. With this type, the correct chain tension, allowing just sufficient free movement in the non-driving strand of the chain, is determined by accurate design and machining in the first place. Over a long mileage wear will take place in the chain joints to an extent which will eventually prejudice the accuracy of valve timing, since the extra slack permits undue movement of the camshaft relative to the crankshaft. The free movement may become excessive from this point of view long before the chain is actually worn out.

With longer shaft centres it is usual to have some form of jockey-wheel or chain tensioner which maintains the correct tension throughout the life of the chain. This is a very desirable feature of a camshaft drive, but some forms of tensioner are far from perfect and in fact this item can set some quite complicated problems. An unrestrained spring device is quite capable of oscillating in sympathy with the chain and the shafts, whereas a correctly designed tensioner always has some form of damping mechanism to prevent this. In addition, the best types incorporate a ratchet or similar motion which, while allowing the spring to " feed " the device on to the chain to take up lost motion due to wear, limits the corresponding backward movement against the spring. (See page 83.)

The few examples of double-camshaft engines using crankcase location for the shafts also have chain drive, in a triangular formation typified by the Lea-Francis described in Chapter 13. The chain is of considerable length, and a tensioner or manually adjusted jockey-wheel is always used. These engines have, of course, two rows of inclined overhead valves, the push-rods and rocker gear being duplicated on either side of the engine. That two camshafts are not necessary for this form of valve layout was, however, demonstrated many years ago by the B.M.W. concern, who mounted a single camshaft in the normal location in the crankcase. A similar arrangement to that of the B.M.W. is to-day used on the Frazer-Nash and Bristol engines. (See diagram below.)

The valves on the "camshaft" side of the block are operated by push-rods and rockers in the usual manner. The valves opposite are actuated by means of near-horizontal

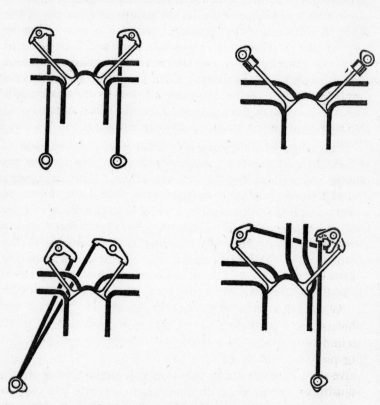

FOUR TYPICAL METHODS OF OPERATING INCLINED O.H.V.: (1) AS ON RILEY AND LEA-FRANCIS; (2) THE WELL-TRIED TWIN-O.H.C. LAYOUT; (3) A TRANS-ATLANTIC METHOD WHICH IS BECOMING INCREASINGLY POPULAR; (4) THE FRAZER-NASH AND BRISTOL ARRANGEMENT, WHICH IS STILL UNIQUE.

push-rods running across the head, which in turn are engaged by bell-crank levers worked by another set of vertical push-rods from the camshaft. Thus, one set of valves uses two push-rods per valve for its operation, but this does not appear to have any disadvantageous effect on the performance of the engine.

Twin overhead-camshaft engines

The twin o.h.c. engine, though famous as a producer of power since the earliest days, was up to a few years ago regarded as an exclusive feature of G.P.-type racing cars and a few highly exclusive sports engines. It is to one firm that credit must justifiably go for putting the type of engine on the market at a price within the reach of many enthusiastic motorists, in the shape of the Jaguar type XK120 power unit. It is of some significance that several other makers are exploring the possibilities of marketing cars with this valve-operating layout. Another well-known example of the type is, of course, the Aston Martin, and it is significant, in assessing relative performances, that this make as well as the Jaguar has had a goodly share of competition successes.

As far as efficiency in valve operation is concerned, the merits of the double-o.h.c. arrangement lie mainly in the substitution of rotary for reciprocating motion right up to the valves. By suitably mounting the two camshafts one above each row of valve stems, a very simple form of attack can be used, either through a light rocking follower or by a short plunger or piston tappet sliding in a guide-hole and bearing against the cam and valve stem at its upper and lower extremities respectively.

With the latter arrangement the need for rocker-shafts is obviated, and extreme lightness can be obtained in the only reciprocating part—the tappet—by making this of a simple one-piece formation, using circular shims under a hardened valve-stem cap, or similar arrangement, for valve clearance adjustment.

The drive to twin overhead-camshafts can take many forms, and in the past such unorthodox devices as the " Y-frame " have appeared. In this arrangement the extremities of the Y are each connected to a crankpin, one on a half-time shaft driven from the crankshaft by gears, and the other two on the two camshafts. Rotation of the half-time crank is thus transmitted to the other two cranks.

Nowadays, either a train of gears or a roller-chain drive is universal, the former being favoured by makers of very high output racing engines, while the latter is almost universal for sports engines and racers developed therefrom. Chain drives are usually in two stages through an intermediate shaft, with suitable tensioners or jockey pinions on each stage of the drive to ensure the minimum of lost motion. (See page 82.)

Single o.h.c. engines

The single o.h.c. engine is not quite so popular to-day as in the past; well-known examples are Singer and A.C. in the high-performance field, the former engine in addition powering the H.R.G. Many of the advantages of the twin o.h.c. arrangement apply equally to one camshaft, though, of course, when inclined valves are being operated it is necessary to use fairly substantial cam-followers or rockers to transmit the motion. In the case of operation of a single row of valves, direct attack can be used, an excellent example of this system being found in Wolseley engines.

Crankshafts

Crankshaft speeds on competition car engines have doubled within the past thirty years. This has obviously not been done without some very remarkable achievements in the way of shaft design, balancing, and metallurgy. Steel shaft forgings are still a prime favourite for the shaft, but great strides have been made in the use of alternative materials variously referred to as semi-steel or high-tensile iron. Neither of these descriptions really does justice to the material of which Meehanite is an example. It is briefly a high-duty iron which by suitable control of its structure in manufacture has imparted to it a strength and wearing quality more than equal to the severest stresses which it will encounter in service. It will be evident that a cast shaft is usually quite a lot less expensive than a forging, but quite apart from this aspect, it is more

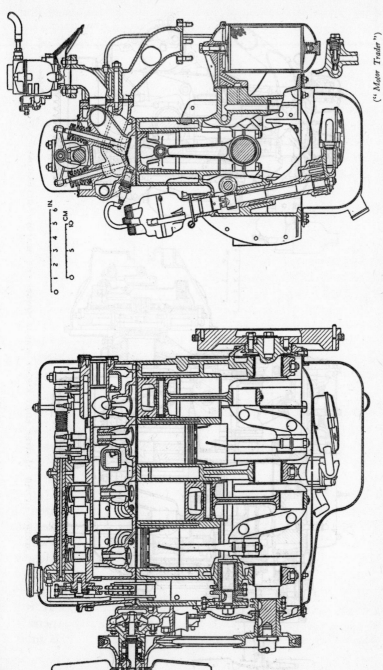

("*Motor Trader*")

SINGLE O.H.C. PRACTICE—THE 1,500-C.C. SINGER.   A MODIFIED VERSION IS USED ON THE H.R.G.

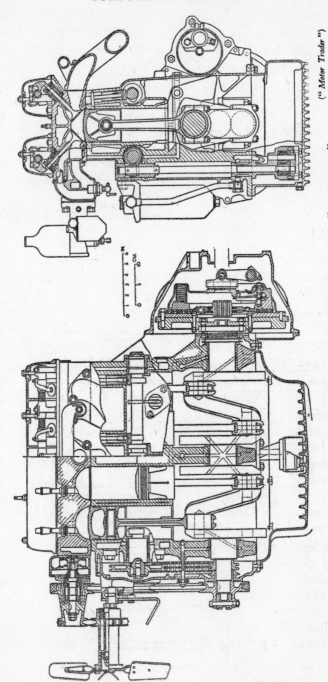

SECTION OF THE 2½-LITRE RILEY ENGINE WHICH POWERS THE HEALEY "SILVERSTONE"

than likely that in the future the iron shaft will give evidence of qualities peculiar to its construction in respect of long bearing journal life and freedom from fatigue.

Apart from the increasing popularity of the cast shaft as an alternative to the steel forging, notable advances have taken place in recent years in balancing technique. Some years ago it was usual to find that the provision of counterbalance weights opposite the crank throws, while in themselves desirable, were liable to bring in problems of torsional vibration, leading to unwanted stresses in the shaft. Auxiliary damping devices fitted as a rule at the fore end of the shaft mitigated this trouble, but in some cases it was preferred to do without the balance-weights rather than risk setting up stresses in other directions. Non-counterbalanced shafts tend to vibrate at high speeds even where a large number of cylinders is concerned, and this vibration must lead eventually to excessive main bearing wear. Counterbalanced shafts are nowadays universal, and this is done without bringing in any of the troubles which could have been expected in past years.

Bearings and materials

As far as main bearings are concerned, some makers remain loyal to the well-tried thick shell-type with suitable white-metal linings. Many years ago this type was, of course, standard practice for both main and big-end bearings, having the advantage that bearing renovation, which usually took the form of closing-in the two bearing halves by machining the mating faces, and then scraping the bearing surfaces to suit a reduced diameter of journal, was facilitated by the construction. Precision machining of surfaces has, however, obviated the need or desirability of such forms of hand fitting.

The introduction of the thin-wall bearing pioneered by Vandervell has resulted in its very wide use for big-ends, and it is also becoming popular for main bearings. As its name implies, this bearing has a thin steel strip forming the backing for the bearing surface, the strip having a thickness of from about .05 to .08 in. The manufacturing process produces an endless strip which is subsequently cut to the required lengths and shaped to conform to the specified bearing contour. Oil grooves, locating tabs and so on, are incorporated during the cutting operation. The actual composition of the bearing surface proper varies with the duty required.

At the final machining operation on thin-wall bearings they are fixed in an exactly similar manner to that in which they will be located in the engine. This ensures that accurate contact between the back of the strip and the housing, which is essential for heat dissipation and equalization of load, will be ensured. As all bearing housings distort slightly when bolted up, another advantage of the thin-wall type lies in its ability to accommodate itself to such minor irregularities. The final machining allows for this, so that when in its working position the fit will be absolutely correct.

One or two makers of sports engines still favour a form of big-end bearing which was popular before the war. This construction involves depositing the bearing metal direct on the eye of the rod without any intervening bearing shell or strip backing. The great advantage of this form of bearing is in the absence of loose parts and the extremely good heat conductivity away from the bearing surface direct to the mass of the rod.

CHAPTER 5

Crankshaft Design

*Bearing location—Problems of balancing—Secondary forces—Balancing the single—
Sixes and eights—Vibration dampers—Bore-stroke ratio*

Bearing location

A high degree of unanimity now exists amongst manu-facturers regarding the most desirable number of main bear-ings and their location. Many years ago, taking four-cylinder engines as typical, high-class types had five bearings, popular quality types three, whilst two only was the hall-mark of cheapness. Obviously, a bearing between each crank-throw does give a very high degree of rigidity to the shaft, when the latter is considered as a beam. However, there is no doubt that the extra length of shaft necessitated by the presence of several main journals, apart from its disadvantages in lengthen-ing the engine as a whole, has other effects not altogether desirable, in rendering the shaft more liable to excessive torsional oscillation, or winding-and-unwinding effect. This disadvantage can be mitigated by the use of robust material and large diameter main journals, but too much emphasis on the latter spells increased frictional losses. As shaft design has improved, the use of three main bearings only on four-cylinder engines has become universal, the absence of the two intermediate bearings being more than compensated for by the mass of metal which, with this form of construction, it is possible to accommodate between adjacent crank-throws, and the overall shortening of the shaft.

Regarding two-bearing shafts, history appears to indicate that—exemplified by the original Austin Seven—cheapness was its inspiration, and for low powers it was quite successful. In spite of the general improvement in shaft design, two bearings ultimately proved unable to give sufficient rigidity to cope with increasing powers and r.p.m. High performance cars like the 1,100 c.c. Riley, and the M.G. type J, appeared in the early 1930s with two-bearing shafts, but they undoubtedly represented the final phase of this type.

Present-day practice for four-cylinder engines is the use of three mains, relatively short " back-to-front," but of fairly large diameter. This proportion makes for the shortest shaft, which in turn implies a compact engine and the ability to use plenty of metal between the crank-throws. For six-cylinder engines most makers seem agreed that four main bearings are ample. This is a logical arrangement, since it is basically the same construction that serves the four-cylinder, and the considerations as to overall length apply with even greater force to the six-in-line.

A notable exception in the six-cylinder category is the XK120 Jaguar. The makers of this power unit have remained faithful to seven bearings since the days of the famous SS100. The high power output of this engine probably owes something to the rigidity of the crankshaft assembly, but on the other hand, there are available four-bearing engines of comparable performance in proportion to their cubic capacity.

Problems of balancing

Reference has already been made to improvements in balancing technique. The underlying theories have, of course, not changed since the early days of multi-cylinder gas-engines, but their application to light-weight high-speed engines with various cylinder arrangements and firing orders has called for a good deal of research work.

When a flexibly mounted engine of modern design is violently accelerated, it rocks on its mountings. Similarly, it tends to wobble when idling if the firing is irregular. These characteristics have nothing to do with balance, but are the result of torque reaction as the engine speed varies. Thus, because a flexibly mounted engine betrays a wobble under some conditions, it does not indicate that the form of mounting is being used to hide an inferior product.

An engine in complete balance does not vibrate except under conditions such as the foregoing, whether its mounting is rigid or flexible. Further, taking the engine as a whole, it can be balanced without the addition of counterweights to the shaft, if the cylinder layout is suitable. For example, a six-cylinder engine with three pairs of pistons at 120 deg. is completely balanced, if it has cylinders 1–6, 2–5, and 3–4, in line at the above relative angle. The normal four-cylinder with cylinders 1–4 and 2–3 " up " and " down " respectively, gives faultless primary balance only; this statement will be amplified later.

Vibration is usually caused by deflection of the crankshaft resulting from the power impulses. Under the influence of the power strokes, the shaft tends to twist and untwist, this phenomenon being known as torsional vibration. There is obviously little that can be done about this, except to make the component so stiff that the amplitude of the vibrations is reduced to the minimum and kept below danger level. The shaft, in rotating, has its own natural frequency of vibration without regard to power impulses, and if the torsional vibration reaches a figure which corresponds to the natural frequency of the shaft, the " swing " (in pendulum parlance) can in theory at all events, reach limitless heights. Such an occurrence will ultimately lead to shaft failure, and to prevent this the torsional deflection is controlled. If the shaft of itself is unable to do this, a vibration damper is fitted.

The provision of balance weights opposite the big-ends on multi-cylinder engines certainly assists in smooth running by reducing the loading on the main bearings. The use of such weights obviously adds to the inertia resistance to rotation of the shaft, and thus to problems of torsional vibration. Another factor in this connection is the length of the shaft in the main bearings, in relation to its diameter. A long bearing has the virtue of giving a good measure of support to the shaft as a beam, but, of course, there is more of the shaft available to twist. This can be kept in check by making the journals of adequate diameter, but in general the shortest possible bearing is preferable, the shaft looking after itself in the matter of beam rigidity.

E

Secondary forces

What we have already referred to as " primary " balance is obtained when the reciprocating masses are moving in opposite directions, as in the case of the normal four-cylinder engine. The angularity of the connecting rod, however, introduces further complications in the form of what are known as " secondary " out-of-balance forces. To understand what these are, it has to be appreciated that, with uniform rotational velocity of the crank, the piston speed is *not* a correspondingly uniform acceleration and deceleration from zero to zero at each end of its stroke. The maximum piston speed is reached when the crank and connecting rod are at right-angles to each other, and this position is obtained when the crank has moved considerably less than 90 deg. from t.d.c., and considerably more than 90 deg. from b.d.c. Thus, it is obvious that the piston must accelerate away from t.d.c. much more rapidly than it does from b.d.c., since it reaches its maximum speed in a shorter portion of the stroke.

These secondary disturbing forces are somewhat complex, but can be rendered innocuous by correct dimensioning of the connecting rod in proportion to the crank-throw. It will be evident that if the connecting rod could be made infinitely long, or a cross-slide motion substituted for the crank, the piston motion would be simple harmonic, that is, its maximum speed would be reached at the middle of the stroke, and its acceleration and deceleration would be equal on either side. In such a case no secondary disturbances would arise. On the other hand, [with a very short connecting rod, the secondaries are increased.

If we consider a normal four-cylinder layout, and imagine pistons 1 and 4 just leaving t.d.c., and numbers 2 and 3 just leaving b.d.c., we can see that the two outer pistons will have reached their maximum velocity, and started to decelerate, while the other two are still accelerating. A little thought will show that, while the movement of the four pistons along their strokes is in primary balance (the two outers being opposed by the two inners travelling oppositely) the secondary forces always act in the same direction, since the pair of pistons leaving t.d.c. will always have started to slow down before the pair nearing b.d.c. have reached their full speed.

Balancing the single

Although we are concerned mainly with multi-cylinder engines, a few words regarding problems of balance associated with single-cylinder engines of the motor-cycle and Formula 3 types will not be out of place. The normal engine of this type cannot be balanced primarily, as there is only one piston. A remarkably efficient compromise is possible, however, and many of these engines run at very high speeds with commendable smoothness. If we imagine such an engine with an unbalanced crank, it will be evident that as the piston reaches top and bottom dead centres it will set up a vibration in the vertical plane, the frequency of this being equal to the r.p.m. of the crank. If a balance weight is fitted opposite the crank, of equal weight to the reciprocating parts, this will neutralize the vibration at two points, t.d.c. and b.d.c. It is only here that the effect will be beneficial. At all other points in the rotation of the crank, the balance weights will be a nuisance, and at 90 deg. either side of the cylinder axis the vibration will be transferred to the horizontal plane to the same degree as it formerly was (without the balance weight) in the vertical plane.

In practice, single cylinder engines usually have very heavy internal flywheel assemblies, providing great rigidity, the balance weights being formed integrally with these. The weight is decided on by trial and error, and comes out at about 65 per cent. of the reciprocating weight, so that as a consequence there is both a vertical and a horizontal unbalanced force. The mass of the engine unit acts as a useful medium in absorbing much of the vibration and there is little doubt that the smooth operation of the modern racing single owes something to the sheer weight of the power unit. High revolutions also assist, and in general the percentage of reciprocating weight included in the balance weights is decreased for high r.p.m. and increased for lower r.p.m., though this is by no means an unvarying rule.

In the case of multi-cylinders a similar state of affairs

exists, that is, each set of counterweights is given a certain percentage of the weight of the reciprocating masses of its particular cylinder.

In these cases, however, the balance weights fulfil a rather different function, since in any case primary balance is obtained by the opposing pistons (in the case of the normal four-in-line). The weights help to reduce load on main bearings, while in horizontally opposed twins of Douglas and Jowett type, they nullify the rocking couple which is the result of the offset of the cylinder axes.

Sixes and eights

The smooth running of the six-in-line is not entirely due to the multiplicity of power impulses. The primary forces are, of course, balanced, as already explained, assuming three pairs of crank-throws at 120 deg. It can also be shown geometrically, without too much difficulty, that the secondary forces are also balanced, and this obviously has an important influence.

The complications with sixes and straight-eights arise not from out-of-balance forces, but from torsional oscillation, which is a result of the long crankshaft necessary with these engines. Firing order has, of course, a considerable bearing on this factor, and in the past some peculiar orders were adopted in an attempt to secure crankshaft reliability. Nowadays, sixes usually fire either 1–5–3–6–2–4 or 1–4–2–6–3–5.

Straight-eight crankshafts can be formed of two orthodox four-cylinder shafts placed, in effect, end-to-end at 90 deg. to each other. There will in such a case be primary balance, since each half of the shaft is balanced by the " two-up-two-down " effect common to the four. However, the secondaries will be troublesome, as they will act downwards in, say, the front half of the engine, and simultaneously upwards in the rear half. Thus the engine will tend to rock horizontally. The remedy is to split one of the " fours " and arrange the combination so that cranks 1–2–7–8 are horizontal when 3–4–5–6 are vertical. The middle of the engine will then be lifted while the two ends are at the same time pushed down, resulting in complete secondary balance.

Vibration dampers

Torsional vibration of crankshafts is undesirable even when it does not reach an amplitude rendering the shaft liable to failure. It is wasteful of power, just as is any other uncalled-for movement. It leads to timing errors between cylinders, since the phasing of the cranks may vary. When the camshaft is driven, as is normal practice, from the front end, quite appreciable divergences in valve timing can be caused, and, of course, the error is by no means constant.

Vibration dampers, sometimes known as detuning wheels, are of several types, but all work on the same general principle, which is that of a small auxiliary flywheel. This item is not mounted rigidly on a hub, but is fitted thereto with some flexible medium interposed. For example, the wheel may be bonded to a rubber disc which is in turn bonded to the hub, or the wheel may be gripped between two spring-loaded faces driven by the hub. (The hub is, of course, keyed or otherwise fixed to the crankshaft at the fore end.) The damper wheel naturally tends to turn with uniform motion, and any oscillation of the shaft, and thus the damper hub, causes relative movement between it and the wheel. This movement is in turn absorbed in friction, and in this way serious oscillations are dissipated. In some cases the rim of the damper wheel forms a pulley from which the drive is taken by belt to the fan and dynamo. This feature not only augments the flywheel effect, but provides a smooth drive to the components concerned.

Bore-stroke ratio

The choice of bore-stroke ratio is one requiring a number of factors to be taken into consideration. There has been of late a tendency to over-simplify the question, when reviewing designs of engines in which a drastic shortening of the stroke has been carried out. Upon investigation it will frequently be found that the dimensions concerned have little or no bearing on the power produced or the overall efficiency of the power unit, and are adopted almost solely from the viewpoint of production costs.

Obviously, the significance of the stroke length is that for a given number of r.p.m., the longer the stroke the higher will be the piston speed, and the latter, in general, represents the limiting factor in the number of r.p.m. that it is possible to obtain from any particular engine. Assuming that the same working pressure can be maintained in the cylinders, the h.p. of any engine will increase in direct proportion to the increase in r.p.m. Thus, if an engine of a specified cubic capacity is redesigned by shortening the stroke, increasing the bore to give the same cubic capacity, and increasing the r.p.m. to give the same piston speed as the original, it will produce more power.

The obvious query, and the point from which design should commence in this respect, is—what piston speed is allowable? This depends on many things : for example, the quality of material, heat to be conducted, weight, and so on. It is by no means true to say that as the piston speed rises, frictional losses increase unduly, that bore wear is influenced or oil consumption becomes excessive. Whilst a figure of 2,000 to 2,500 f.p.m. is often quoted as a typical " cruising " piston speed, it is easily demonstrable that engines of high-grade type can exceed this figure for indefinite periods with complete satisfaction, while racing engines have approached 5,000 f.p.m. without disaster. For vehicles in the popular price class it is, of course, essential to limit piston speeds to figures in keeping with the materials, bearing areas, and so on, that are employed. This is, however, a matter of commercial expediency and not of engine design as we are considering it.

When comparing different stroke lengths, it is an excellent idea to forget about piston speeds and consider other design features. The effect on general engine dimensions will be apparent, and there is no need to go into such items. As far as combustion chambers are concerned, we need not worry too much about the relative areas exposed to the gases (as shown in Chapter 2). We may well find, however, that for the chosen compression ratio, an increase in stroke length will enable a better piston crown shape to be achieved than would be possible on a bigger-bore engine, and with modern fuels enabling high ratios to be used, this is an important point.

Otherwise, the bore and stroke dimensions should have little influence on the robustness of the power unit in respect of rigidity, bearing area, durability, and so forth. If adequate attention is given to such points, there is no reason why the stroke should not be as long as can be allowed, commensurate with the required piston speed. This latter should be kept as high as reasonable, so obtaining the maximum thermal efficiency, and if the design is right to start with, the only valid reason for shortening the stroke will be to obtain more r.p.m., and thus more power, for the same piston speed.

For an excellent example of this, we can turn to the racing motor-cycle field. The famous Norton 500-c.c. engine for many years used a 100-mm. stroke, reaching its peak around 1937. The stroke was then shortened to 94 mm., with a proportionate increase in r.p.m., and power. In 1950 the stroke went down to 90 mm., in 1952 to 86 mm., and in 1953 to 82 mm., in each case with beneficial results to the power curve. To all intents and purposes, the piston speed remained unaltered throughout the years of development— a perfect example of very clear thinking and single-minded attention to sensible design.

CHAPTER 6

Planning for Performance

Performance data—Cylinder head design—Efficient scavenging—
Overhead valve layouts—Compression ratio and heat loss—
Turbulence features with o.h.v. head—A popular type—Considerations of gas flow—
O.h. inlet, side exhaust valve arrangements—
The inclined-o.h.v. combustion chamber—High compression ratios—
Spark plug position

Performance data

We have considered in an earlier chapter the basic theoretical requirements for usage of the heat value of the fuel to the utmost advantage. In the next few pages we will examine some of the problems which beset designers in arriving at a satisfactory compromise, not only in relating desirable factors in performance, but in making the results available at a reasonable price.

At one time, many motor-car makers were rather reticent on the subject of engine performance figures, whereas to-day most catalogues give full details of b.h.p. and r.p.m., torque, and so on. This is all to the good, but perhaps it is inevitable that we may find minor snags associated with this comprehensive data.

To take just one example—maximum b.h.p. at so many r.p.m. It can be assumed that the former is the highest power developed, and the latter represents somewhere near the top limit in safe r.p.m. If the axle ratio and effective wheel diameter are known, a simple calculation will enable the maximum speed of the car to be assessed. This is sometimes rather at variance with the claimed maximum, while on occasion it may be found that the claimed b.h.p. is simply not sufficient to propel the car at its supposed maximum speed.

That some horses have longer legs than others is a comment attributed to one or two famous racing men who were asked how they achieved success on what were considered relatively modest power outputs. As a general rule, the b.h.p. figures quoted by makers in normal literature do not give details as to how the figures are obtained. Common sense suggests, of course, that they are engine test-bed figures, but then the point arises as to whether the engine so tested is encumbered with dynamo, fan, water pump, clutch and so on. All these are necessary on the car, but not on the test bed.

Although high figures for b.h.p. and r.p.m. maxima sound impressive, it is at least of equal importance to know the figures at other points on the power curve. Further, while we have become reconciled to speedometers which apparently cannot be fitted to certain makes of car without immediately adding 10 per cent. to the maximum speed, it would be a pity if a similar state of affairs is allowed to develop when quoting engine performance figures. These remarks are prompted by the fact that when engaged in " private " engine development it is by no means unusual to find the performance of standard engines woefully below the catalogued figures. Since in all cases the cars themselves perform perfectly satis- factorily in terms of m.p.h. and acceleration, such exaggera- tion seems quite pointless.

Apart from sheer horse-power, there are many other factors which affect the car's roadworthiness. Weight is important, and wind resistance is nowadays receiving proper attention. Well-chosen gear ratios can transform both driving effort and performance. Flywheel weight, length of piston stroke, and many other design features may determine whether the engine is alert and lively on the throttle, or whether it takes time to work up to speed.

Cylinder head design

The side-valve engine is still very popular in the sphere of competition motoring, particularly (in the small four- cylinder category) in this country. It has, of course, enjoyed a long run of popularity amongst American manufacturers of large vehicles of over 3.5 litres cubic capacity. In these cases, simplicity and economy of manufacture have influenced the choice of layout, and it is significant that, with improvements in fuel technology continually taking place, makers in the U.S.A. have latterly shown that they are fully appreciative of the fact that full advantage of such fuels can be gained only in engines of the o.h.v. type, and that nowhere in the world is fuel so plentiful that its inefficient use in quantity can be considered a substitute for power obtained by efficient burning.

Irrespective of cubic capacity, makers of side-valve engines are, in general, unanimous in their choice of head design. Due to the necessity of having a chamber at the side of the cylinder in which the valves can operate, there is inevitably a considerable free volume at t.d.c. If, in addition to this valve chamber, a combustion chamber is also incorporated directly above the piston at t.d.c., the ratio of clearance volume to swept volume becomes so small that reasonably high compression ratios are impossible of achievement. In the old days of low speed, large-capacity engines, in which compression ratios of 4 : 1 or so were considered adequate, such a head shape was fairly commonplace. Such techniques as the continuation of turbulence throughout the induction and compression strokes were virtually unknown, and although some experimentation with regard to spark plug position took place, this component usually ended up directly above the inlet valve, where it received the benefit of the cool incoming mixture. Possibly the latter also gained something from the heat extracted from the plug.

The modern side-valve head not only permits of quite high compression ratios, but provides for a goodly degree of turbulence. This is achieved by concentrating the bulk of the clearance space over the valves and the passage connecting the valve chamber with the cylinder. The head above the cylinder bore is of flat formation so that when the piston is at t.d.c., there is only a little more than running clearance between the piston and head. Thus, as the piston approaches t.d.c. of the compression stroke, there is a high-speed egress of mixture from this space in the direction of the valve chamber; in other words, a " squish," to use the common and expressive term.

This high-velocity gas movement augments the turbulence already existing (in good designs) as a result of the port layout, and should be still effective at the moment of ignition. Thus, providing the spark plug is located in the best position, quick flame propagation and efficient combustion will result.

Efficient scavenging

This type of cylinder head also gives a high scavenge efficiency. It will be appreciated that at t.d.c. of the exhaust stroke the " squish " will comprise exhaust gases, and will

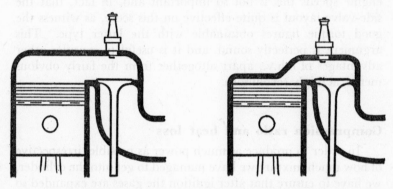

THE DIAGRAMS SHOW (ON LEFT) THE OLD TYPE OF LOW COMPRESSION SIDE VALVE HEAD, AND (RIGHT) THE MODERN VERSION

again take place from the cylinder towards the valve chamber and the open exhaust valve. Whilst the limitations of the side-valve type are felt at high revolutions, and on engines using high working pressures, where considerable heat flow has to be catered for, it does give a remarkably smooth and economical performance together with excellent torque figures, particularly at part-throttle running.

The simplicity of the side-valve layout has many times induced designers to endeavour to improve its thermal efficiency without departing from the basic arrangement. However, no practical design has yet been evolved which is superior to that just described, which was developed by Sir Harry Ricardo many years ago.

Overhead valve layouts

For maximum efficiency, meaning the conversion of as much of a given quantity of fuel into power as possible, together with high power output, there is no question about the merits of the valve-in-head arrangement. It is usual when considering what advantages accrue to the o.h.v. type, to refer to the disposition of the valves as an aid to good cylinder filling at the higher end of the r.p.m. range, when the time intervals for induction and exhaust strokes are ever-shortening. It can, however, be argued that at average engine speeds this is not so important and, in fact, that the side-valve layout is quite effective on this score, as witness the good torque figures obtainable with the latter type. This argument is perfectly sound, and it is useful to consider other advantages of o.h.v., apart altogether from the fairly obvious merits at high revolutions.

Compression ratio and heat loss

In order to produce as much power as possible, irrespective of how much mixture we have managed to get into the cylinder, we have to ensure that after ignition the gases are expanded so as to produce the maximum pressure on the piston throughout the length of the working stroke. In meeting this requirement, we know that the comp. r. should be as high as possible, and also the pressure before ignition. In addition, the heat loss to the surrounding metal must be the minimum possible.

As far as the last-named point is concerned, we have shown in Chapter 2 that very little power can be gained even if all heat loss could be stopped. However, in regard to comp. r., a reasonable mechanical layout of o.h.v. head will allow up to 12 : 1 without difficulty. In other words, the comp. r. is governed mainly by the type of fuel used, and not, as is the case with the side-valve design, by mechanical considerations.

The advantage of the o.h.v. head in allowing a relatively unimpeded entry and exit for the gases is evident from a study of the line drawings of typical engines included in these pages. Further, with the two valves positioned in the head, it is possible to vary the positions of the components within a wide range, and also to design the combustion chamber and piston crown to promote turbulence. Altering the position of the spark plug in relation to one or both valves can effect a considerable change in the engine's characteristics. Likewise, the provision of a " squish " area at one or both sides of the head, with the resultant draught, as it were, directed as desired, can also have advantageous consequences. It is worth while investigating some of the possible arrangements, before going more deeply into the technicalities thereof.

Using a normally situated camshaft mounted in the crankcase, push-rod and rocker operation in its simplest form calls for the valves to be arranged in a single row, more or less along the centre-line of the head. Usually, all the ports for both induction and exhaust are brought out to one side, this making for simplicity of manufacture and ease of hot-spotting the induction manifold from the adjacent exhaust, where this is considered desirable. Both valves in each cylinder therefore open into the combustion chamber directly above the pistons.

In earlier engines of the type, the combustion chamber consisted of what amounted to an extension of the cylinder bore, that is, circular in plan. It being impracticable to mount the spark plug centrally in the head, due to the small amount of room between the valve seats, the plug was carried horizontally at one side, usually the side remote from the ports. It will be obvious that this form of combustion chamber was devoid of any " squish " feature, but had a refreshing absence of pockets, and generous spaces around the valves. Due to the spark plug position, the rate of flame travel was found to be considerably affected by engine speed and throttle opening, and the best results were apparent when a hand ignition control was provided for use at lower r.p.m. Mixture strength somewhat on the rich side was also desirable, for the same reason. Evidently the degree of turbulence set up in this head shape was limited, and although the performance could be improved by experimenting with the plug position, the general arrangement gives little scope for this. The shape has thus been generally superseded by types which, with no extra complication, show improved results in the ability to burn weaker mixtures, and having less sensitivity to ignition timing.

Turbulence features with o.h.v. head

A simple and effective method of introducing a head shape to promote turbulence, and one which seems to have been a logical step in development, without departing from the same basic layout as the one described, is to make the chamber containing the valves (and forming the combustion chamber) of slightly less width, in the dimension at right-angles to the crankshaft, than the bore diameter. This means in effect that the flat face of the cylinder head, when in position, forms a ceiling on two opposite sides of the bore, which is just clear of the piston at t.d.c. It will be evident that this " squish " feature, as well as promoting turbulence, reduces the area of the clearance space in comparison with the type previously described, and this enables very high compression ratios to be used if desired, without the need for an abnormally long stroke. The spark plug, though still positioned at the side, has moved inward with the reduction in head width, thus coming nearer the valves.

An obvious objection to this layout is that the valves may tend to be cramped, and if breathing is unduly restricted, volumetric efficiency will suffer, so losing much of the benefit of the improved turbulence. It is important, therefore, in seeking after the latter, not to make the valve space too small. As a matter of fact, early engines of this type did not show by any means the hoped-for advantages over the earlier type, mainly because of breathing restriction. We shall see from later investigations that as far as it is possible to draw conclusions from a study of valve arrangements, the chief requirement is to get the gas in and out with as little restriction as possible, and all other aids to efficient combustion, desirable as they are, must not prejudice this.

Without departing from the simplicity of the single row of valves in the head, it is possible to arrive at a type of combustion chamber which, in respect of both high torque figures and good full-power output, is not very far behind layouts of much more complicated form. A slight deviation of the valves from the vertical will provide a freer entry and exit to and from the valve ports. At the same time, if the valves are moved slightly away from the centre line of the head, and the " squish " area concentrated opposite the spark plug, which is situated on the deepest side of the combustion chamber, it will be evident that several desirable conditions

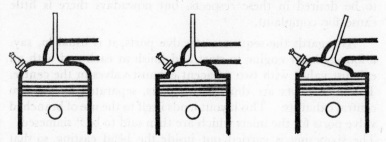

THE EVOLUTION OF THE " SQUISH " FORM OF O.H.V. HEAD IS SHOWN IN THESE DIAGRAMS

have been fulfilled. First, the all-important requirement of free gas entry and exit has been met. Secondly, a high degree of turbulence will be set up in the direction of the spark plug, which, together with the deep section of the chamber around the plug, will give an adequately large flame-front area to ensure uniform and complete combustion. At the same time, the shape of the combustion chamber is still of such form that high compression ratios are practicable.

A popular type

The illustrations above show in diagrammatic form the three types of o.h.v. head described, and reveal the essential differences. Though type A is little used nowadays, types B and C are extremely popular amongst sports engines in every price class, this being undoubtedly due to the fact that experience has shown their capabilities in providing extremely high performance.

With all the ports arranged on one side of the head, there will inevitably be considerable inequality of temperature. Much thought has therefore been devoted to using plenty of metal at the right places, and having the cooling water flow directed to the hotter spots. Distortion due to temperature variations does not necessarily lead to cracking of the casting, but can be troublesome in causing loss of power through valve leakage, increased friction, piston ring blow-by, and so on. The vicinity of the exhaust valve is an obvious danger spot, as are any points where there is a thickness of metal not split up by water passages. At one time, head design left something to be desired in these respects, but nowadays there is little cause for complaint.

As regards the sequence of valve ports, it is usual in, say, a four-cylinder engine to start and finish at each end with an exhaust valve, with two adjacent exhaust valves in the centre. The inlet valves are thus in two pairs, separated by the two central exhausts. This layout lends itself to the use of branched valve ports for the inlets which are then said to be " siamesed." The siamesing is carried out inside the head casting, so that on the outside of the four-cylinder head, two ports only will connect to the inlet manifold. The same procedure can be applied to the two middle exhaust ports, resulting in only three exhaust outlets. Siamesing of exhaust ports has the objection that a very hot spot is unavoidable between the ports near the exit, and it is preferable if at all possible to keep exhaust ports entirely separate.

Considerations of gas-flow

Theoretically it is, of course, desirable to have separate ports to avoid as much as possible interference between cylinders due to the overlapping strokes. This is particularly the case on the inlet side, as the overlapping is liable to lead to incorrect mixture distribution as regards both quality and quantity. Equal mixture charging of all cylinders is, of course, an ideal which is never realized in practice, as far as atmospherically charged engines are concerned. A separate carburetter and inlet port to each cylinder gets as near to perfection as possible in this respect. In actual fact, it is doubtful if the much-maligned siamesed inlet ports with a two-branch manifold are any worse than four separate ports with a four-branch pipe, providing that the proportions are correct for the required gas velocity.

(*Continued on page* 97)

CHARGING PAR EXCELLENCE. THE 500-C.C. NORTON INTAKE AND EXHAUST
BRANCHES. NOTE INCLINATION OF THE FORMER

REVERSE-CONE MEGAPHONE ON TAILPIPE OF 500-C.C. RACING CAR, TO ASSIST
EXTRACTOR EFFECT

F

THE TIMING DRIVE OF THE XK120 JAGUAR. A SPRING BLADE TENSIONER IS FITTED
TO THE FIRST STAGE OF THE DRIVE. AN ADJUSTABLE JOCKEY, SEEN BETWEEN THE
CAMSHAFTS, CONTROLS THE TENSION OF THE SECOND STAGE

THE TIMING DRIVE OF THE 2½-LITRE RILEY. THE CHAIN TENSION IS CON-
TROLLED BY A RENOLD AUTO-ADJUSTER WITH RATCHET RESTRAINT MECHANISM

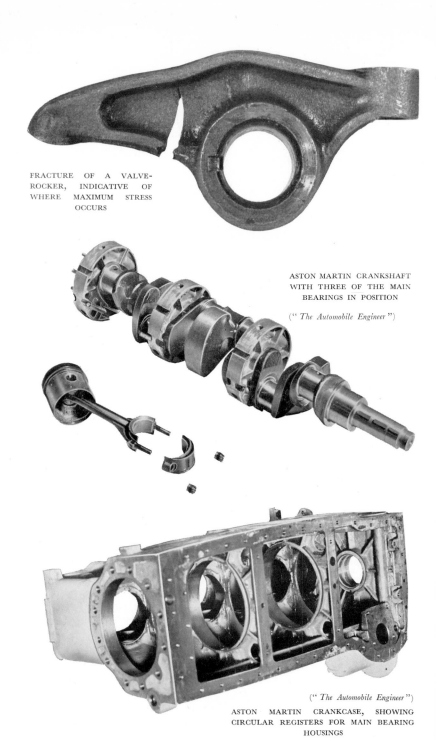

FRACTURE OF A VALVE-
ROCKER, INDICATIVE OF
WHERE MAXIMUM STRESS
OCCURS

ASTON MARTIN CRANKSHAFT
WITH THREE OF THE MAIN
BEARINGS IN POSITION

(" *The Automobile Engineer* ")

(" *The Automobile Engineer* ")

ASTON MARTIN CRANKCASE, SHOWING
CIRCULAR REGISTERS FOR MAIN BEARING
HOUSINGS

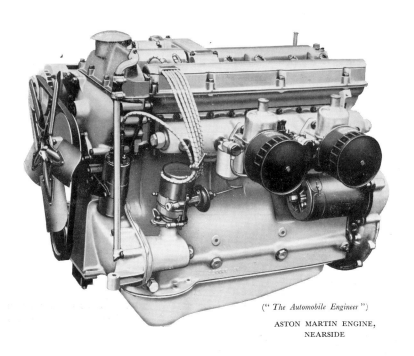

ASTON MARTIN ENGINE,
NEARSIDE

ASTON MARTIN ENGINE,
OFFSIDE

100/B ENGINE WHICH POWERS THE BRISTOL 404

INLET ROCKERS ON BRISTOL ENGINE. NOTE CROSS-OVER PUSH-RODS TO EXHAUST ROCKERS

THE BRISTOL 2-LITRE
ENGINE, TYPE 100/A
(SOLEX CARBURETTERS)

THE BRISTOL 2-LITRE ENGINE, TYPE 85/A (S.U. CARBURETTERS)

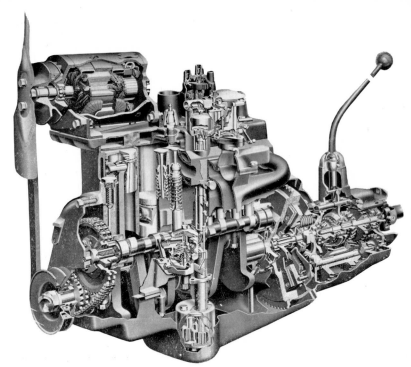

A CUT-AWAY VIEW OF THE 1,172-C.C. FORD ENGINE

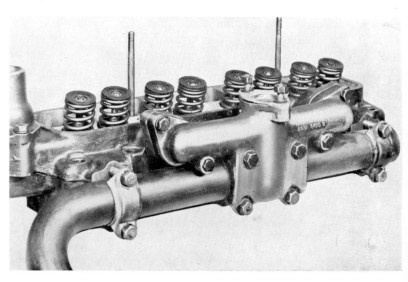

(" *The Automobile Engineer* "

FORD " CONSUL " MANIFOLD LAYOUT

FORD "PREFECT" 1,172-C.C. ENGINE, NEARSIDE

(" *The Automobile Engineer* ")

FORD "CONSUL" CYLINDER BLOCK AND HEAD SHOWING COMBUSTION CHAMBERS

(" The Automobile Engineer ")
NEARSIDE VIEW OF FORD " CONSUL " ENGINE

(" The Automobile Engineer ")
JAGUAR COMBUSTION CHAMBERS
JAGUAR CYLINDER HEAD WITH CAMSHAFT IN POSITION

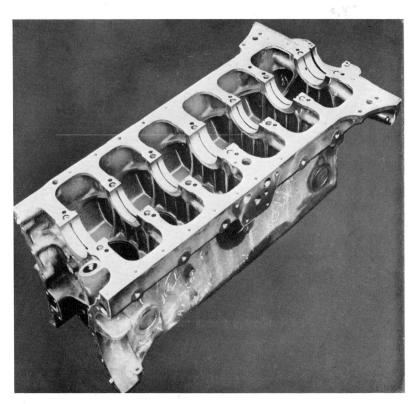

THE SEVEN MAIN BEARING HOUSINGS OF THE JAGUAR XK120 ENGINE

JAGUAR CAMSHAFT AND ASSOCIATED COMPONENTS

(" *The Automobile Engineer* ")

THE 3½-LITRE JAGUAR XK120, OFFSIDE

(" *The Automobile Engineer* ")

THE 3½-LITRE JAGUAR XK120, NEARSIDE

THE LEA-FRANCIS ROCKER GEAR. NOTE ALSO CENTRAL POSITION OF SPARK PLUGS

THE LEA-FRANCIS CRANKCASE AND CYLINDER BLOCK CASTING WITH MAIN BEARING CAPS IN POSITION

("*The Automobile Engineer*")

THE 2½-LITRE LEA-FRANCIS ENGINE, OFFSIDE

("*The Automobile Engineer*")

ON THE LEA-FRANCIS, THREE ALTERNATIVE COMPRESSION RATIOS ARE OBTAINABLE
BY DIFFERENT HEIGHTS OF PISTON CROWN

("*The Automobile Engineer*")

THE 2½-LITRE LEA-FRANCIS ENGINE,
NEARSIDE

("*The Automobile Engineer*")

THE LEA-FRANCIS COMBUSTION CHAMBERS. THE TAPPET FEET CAN ALSO BE SEEN

("*The Automobile Engineer*")

CHAIN DRIVE TO TWIN CAMSHAFTS ON THE 2½-LITRE LEA-FRANCIS
ENGINE

As regards the exhaust side, it seems to be only very recently that due regard has been given to the possibilities of improving performance and reliability by attention to manifold design.   Formerly, at least in the case of more " ordinary " engines, a straight cast manifold bolted along the ports, and having an outlet flange at one end, was considered adequate and has in fact survived to the present day.   With such an arrangement it is possible for inter-cylinder flow to take place, leading to undesirable pressure waves in the manifold.   During the overlap period at the end of the exhaust stroke, such pressures can upset the inlet phase, with a corresponding reduction in the weight of charge drawn in.   Thus, it is not just a case of a little more back pressure on the exhaust stroke, but a definite power loss, and lower volumetric efficiency than need be.   It is much better practice to aim at keeping the exhausts separate until they are well away from the cylinders.   In other words, the modern " bunch of bananas " system of manifolding favoured by many engine tuners is a sensible piece of designing.

Overhead-inlet, side-exhaust valve arrangements

The overhead-inlet valve, with the exhaust valve occupying the traditional side location, is a very old layout.   No doubt originally the object was to facilitate entry of the inlet charge by providing a directional port combined with an adequately large valve, at the same time retaining some of the simplicity of the side-valve engine.   No doubt, too, the fact that exhaust valve breakage was not so liable to have disastrous consequences had something to do with this choice of layout.

As originally designed it was usual to have the inlet valve directly above the exhaust, i.e., a vertical line would pass through both valve stems.   Some cooling was thereby imparted to the hot exhaust valve head by the incoming charge.   The narrow passage between valve chamber and cylinder restricted breathing in much the same way as was the case in the early side-valve engines.   Modern versions of the type have the inlet valve positioned approximately centrally over the cylinder bore, thus enabling the spark plug to be located somewhere near the exhaust valve, which has the effect of

G

igniting the hottest part of the charge first, and shortening the flame path. An excellent example of this arrangement was the Coventry-Climax unit fitted to the pre-war Morgan 4-4, and accounting for an excellent performance.

The adoption of the same layout by Rolls-Royce and Bentley a few years ago somewhat naturally focused attention on the merits of the design. A rather more unorthodox conception is provided by the Rover power unit. Since its inception a few years ago, this engine has shown a performance completely justifying its originality; there is no doubt that the cylinder head arrangement is responsible for the excellent power output.

It is not difficult to see, from a study of the Rover design, that it " started " with the spark plug, and that the combustion chamber was quite literally designed around this component. Thus, the ideal of minimum flame travel, plus almost equal travel in any direction, was achieved. As the cylinder head, or roof of the chamber, is completely flat, there is virtually no limitation on inlet valve size and a very free space around the valve. When the inlet valve is closed, it forms, along with the flat head, a very large " squish " area, the outflow from which is directed at the spark plug.

The exhaust valve, set at about 60 deg. from the vertical, enables the combustion chamber to be of compact form, and obviates the need for a valve pocket, at the same time allowing generous water spaces. Finally, the angles of both valves give directional porting little if any inferior to that obtained on inclined-valve o.h.v. engines.

The inclined-o.h.v. combustion chamber

The next valve layout to be described is one which is a favourite amongst enthusiasts for high-efficiency engines, and with good reason. The o.h.v. engine with hemispherical combustion chambers and both valves inclined in the head is almost as old as the four-stroke cycle, and has been the natural choice of racing engine designers for about fifty years. The type is now making inroads not only in the popular sports car field, but also as a unit for propelling luxurious closed coachwork. It has always been noted for high maximum power output, but the absence of any " squish " features making for control of turbulence has possibly prejudiced the design in the eyes of people to whom smoothness and good torque at low speeds were matters of major importance. It has now been realized that the design possesses remarkable features of what might be termed natural turbulence, making for general all-round excellence in the matter of combustion and expansion which, allied to its good volumetric efficiency characteristics, render the design desirable from almost every point of view.

The general layout will be familiar to readers. The valves are mounted in the head, making an equal angle on either side of the centre line of the cylinder bore, usually not less than 60 deg. nor more than 90 deg. (measured as between the axes of the valve stems). The ports are opposed, the inlets being on one side of the head and the exhausts on the other. In order to allow of adequately large valves it is sometimes necessary to mount the sparking plug in a rather unfavourable position to one side, instead of in the theoretically desirable position in the centre of the head.

The ability of this type of head to maintain good power outputs at high r.p.m. is, of course, due to a very large extent to the extremely good breathing afforded by the easy flow in and out of the valve ports, and the unrestricted entry and exit, the circumferences of the valves being undisturbed by the proximity of cylinder or combustion chamber walls. This is, however, by no means the whole story. With the valve angle, particularly the inlet valve, designed with due regard for operating conditions, it is possible to direct the flow of ingoing mixture so that it is directed into the cylinder bore. With this feature, if in addition the gas velocity can be held to the required figure, it is possible to keep the inlet valve open for an appreciable time after the piston has started to ascend on the up-stroke of compression, without reversal of the gas flow. Similarly, at the end of the exhaust stroke, the overlap period, with both valves open, can be extended over a long period of crank movement, the induction of the descending piston on the inlet stroke being augmented to a marked degree by the extractor action of the exhaust gas column.

This feature applies, of course, on any engine, particularly of the o.h.v. type, but there is no doubt that the inclined-o.h.v. layout enables the fullest advantage to be taken of the phenomenon.

Although not so important nowadays as in early times, a further aid to reliability at high speeds is provided by the relationship between the two valves. The inlet, being directly opposite the exhaust, can be expected to direct some of its flow of relatively cool gas on to the hot exhaust valve. Besides helping to keep down the valve temperature, this characteristic helps to " fry " any wet globules in the inlet gas stream.

High compression ratios

It will be evident that in view of the fairly considerable volume of the hemispherical head, high compression ratios will require careful designing technique. Obviously, a flat-top piston is desirable, and if the stroke of the engine is sufficiently long, such a shape may give the desired ratio. It must be borne in mind, however, that, apart from any question of piston speed, too long a stroke may reduce the bore diameter unduly, making adequate valve sizes impossible to accommodate. In practice it is frequently necessary to adopt a very slightly convex shape of piston crown to take up some of the head space. Some pistons are also provided with cut-aways to enable the valve edge at its lowest point to fully clear the piston at t.d.c.

Although, as mentioned earlier, there is no provision in the hemispherical type of head for any form of " squish," a remarkable degree of turbulence is in fact obtained. This is bound up with careful planning of inlet port shape and direction. It has already been stated that by suitable design, it is possible to induce the gas to flow in to take the maximum advantage of valve overlap without wastage through the exhaust. Similarly, looking at the combustion chamber in plan view, the charge may be directed slightly to one side of the chamber instead of aiming it, as it were, straight at the exhaust valve. By giving the gas a bias to one side, a definite swirl can be set up, and by placing the spark plug in correct relationship to this, extremely good torque figures are obtainable at medium revolutions, without losing any of the good points of the design as far as maximum speeds are concerned.

Spark plug position

The hemispherical head has been criticized at times on the score that it does not give much scope for variation in the position of the spark plug. With the reduction in size of that component which takes place occasionally (but which designers do not always take advantage of), less space is taken up, but it is true to say that the head is fairly well filled up with the two valves. However, an approximately central position for the plug is usually achieved, difficulties formerly encountered in protecting the h.t. leads and plug insulation being suitably dealt with on modern engines.

CHAPTER 7

Combustion Chamber Layout

*Improving performance—Breathing—Inlet valve size—Inlet port characteristics—
Combustion chamber requirements—Exhaust pressure—The influence of plug position
—Ignition current—Coils and plugs*

Improving performance

In the previous chapter we have reviewed in general terms
the main characteristics which distinguish various types of
combustion chamber. It is now proposed to consider what
possibilities are open to improving the performance of these
layouts, and the points meriting attention.

Considering racing machinery for a moment, it is a fact
that unsupercharged engines are to-day turning out as much
power as blown units were doing not very many years ago.
Horse-power is still on the increase without much change in
the basic design of engines. Obviously this increase is coming
from somewhere. The elementary truth is that in order to
obtain power we burn a fuel-air vapour mixture; the more
of this we burn in a given time, the more power we shall get.
Though elementary, this is a most difficult problem to grapple
with.

Breathing

In burning the mixture we have obviously to pass it through
the engine cylinders and to perform the operating cycle in so
doing. We can pass it through, burning it indifferently, at
astronomical revolutions, and obtain a certain amount of
power. On the other hand, we can burn it more efficiently
at lower revs, and quite probably find we have the same
amount of power available. Best of all, we can both burn it
efficiently and obtain an adequate range of r.p.m.

In considering how best to obtain the maximum power for
each charge expanded in the cylinder, it is necessary to start
with the atmosphere. (We are considering unsupercharged

engines; blowing will be dealt with in a later chapter.) We
are using the atmosphere for charging; its pressure is available
for nothing, and provides unlimited quantities of air. If we
can manage to allow the pressure to push the air into the
cylinders in the proper manner we shall go a long way towards
getting full value from the subsequent expansion, since the
speed at which the air enters, and its direction, have considerable bearing on turbulence, which latter is an essential of
good combustion.

The conditions inside the combustion chamber and the
actual shape of the cylinder head and so on, certainly influence
to a goodly extent the efficiency of the expansion process, but
modern o.h.v. heads do not vary very much in this respect.
As already stated, the excellent power outputs obtained from
such types as the inclined-o.h.v. hemispherical head are due
far more to the excellent breathing afforded by this layout
than to the shape of the chamber inside.

It was shown in Chapter 2 that claims of high thermal
efficiencies from certain head designs, based on the use of a
so-called " compact " form of chamber presenting the minimum surface area to the gases, had little basis in fact, and
that even if all the heat lost could be trapped, the nett gain
would be under 3 per cent. on the thermal efficiency figure.
Any modern form of head, irrespective of the valve arrangement, permits only the minimum jacket loss, and no one
particular form shows outstanding advantages in this respect.
It is in the port arrangement, and not in their area of metal,
that well-designed heads reap the benefit of high thermal
efficiency figures.

As we have previously said, we start the charging process
at the air intake. From this point, right up to the moment of
ignition, the mixture should, ideally, be in a state of agitation,
or turbulence. Upon this depends the rate and completeness
of combustion. If we imagine an engine inhaling a charge
which is completely devoid of movement after passing into
the cylinder and being compressed, it is not difficult to visualize
that the area of mixture ignited by the spark plug will burn
relatively slowly and take time to spread throughout the gas.
Such a contingency would be unacceptable even in a slow-
speed engine, as the mixture would probably still be burning

when the exhaust valve opened. The whole speed of combustion and the pressure rise generated by it, is dependent on turbulence. Further, this is true not only under conditions of wide throttle and high speed, when the gas speed through the inlet port will obviously promote the desired disturbances. On light throttle and low speed we still need complete combustion, and it is under these conditions that good head and port design show to advantage.

The design of the inlet port and valve presents several problems. For high volumetric efficiency (which is the inhalation of the maximum weight of charge in a given time) a large valve is called for. This provision also reduces the pumping work necessary. On the other hand, the importance of turbulence has already been emphasized, and for this, a high gas speed is required, which means a reduced size of valve. A balance has thus to be arrived at in determining the size of inlet valve, since it is no use obtaining a high volumetric efficiency and reduction of pumping losses if the combustion and expansion processes are going to suffer due to insufficient agitation of the mixture. In practice it is not difficult to arrive at a figure for gas speed through the valve (actually in the neighbourhood of 140 ft. per second) which promotes good turbulence, without causing losses in the other departments.

Inlet valve size

It is evident from the above reasoning that light-hearted increases of inlet valve size should not be undertaken without full consideration of all that is involved. It must be obvious that an increase in valve diameter of a few millimetres can have no effect on the initial cost of a car. Hearing from some enthusiasts of the tremendous advantages accruing from such a modification, some readers may well have wondered why the makers had not thought of it. The point is, that an increase in valve size may show an increase in b.h.p. at the highest revolutions on wide throttle openings. In a car used almost exclusively under such conditions, a modification may be well worth while. Lower down the speed range, however, the reduction in turbulence may lower the available torque so that acceleration from very low revs can quite easily be inferior to that of the unmodified engine.

The highest volumetric efficiency is obtained when the inlet valve opens straight into the combustion chamber. This feature obtains on all o.h.v. types, but there is more liability for the valve to be a little cramped on the popular all-valves-in-a-row head, than on engines where there are two rows of valves. The overhead inlet, side-exhaust valve layout is, of course, outstanding in providing a very free entry for the inlet gases, since the valve can be placed in the head to the best possible advantage as it is the only one to be thus accommodated. The Rover engine, as mentioned on page 98, is an excellent example of this design.

The side-valve engine can, as already remarked, be designed with a combustion chamber shape to give an adequate compression ratio within fairly normal limits, but it is obvious that in regard to volumetric efficiency the position of the valves and in particular the inlet valve, must prejudice it in comparison with the o.h.v. or overhead-inlet valve type of engine. In the modern side-valve head the bulk of the clearance space is located above the valves, but even so, the incoming mixture has to turn several corners and its direction tends to make it impinge on the inside walls. Excellent turbulence is, of course, obtainable, due possibly to the somewhat tortuous passage of the incoming gas, but it is unquestionable that on sheer volumetric efficiency the valve-in-head types must score, as the inlet takes place into a clear space above the piston.

Inlet port characteristics

The shape and direction of the inlet port in o.h.v. engines has naturally a considerable influence on the degree of turbulence obtained, and much experimental work has been carried out in this direction. Although existing data can give a reliable guide to the results expected from any particular formation, much of the work in the laboratories consists of painstaking trials with various dimensions and shapes of port, noting their influence on the air-flow through the set-up. As an example of what can be achieved in this connection, the

Jaguar XK120 engine can be mentioned. This engine is well known for its excellent power output, but equally creditable are the fuel consumption figures obtained. A close investigation of the inlet port shape (see below) reveals the amount of thought which has gone into the design, the result of close collaboration between the Jaguar concern and the Weslake laboratories. In plan, the inlet ports are slightly tapered towards the entry to increase the gas speed. Additionally, the port (again looking down on the head in plan) does not enter the cylinder dead across its diameter, but slightly to one side, the port then following a curved path to the valve opening. This curvature has a great influence on

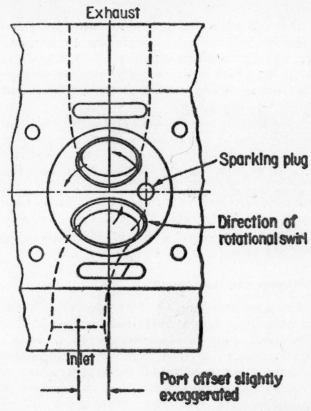

Exhaust

Sparking plug

Direction of rotational swirl

Inlet

Port offset slightly exaggerated

("*The Autocar*")

THE JAGUAR PORT DESIGN IS AIMED AT PRODUCING A HIGH DEGREE OF TURBULENCE the degree of swirl imparted to the mixture. Finally the valve seat itself, the valve shape, and the amount of valve guide projection into the port, are all laid out to form the minimum obstruction.

The above has been quoted as just one example of adequate care being taken in designing an important item. Nowadays most designers devote quite a lot of time to such matters, but some results are better than others, and in general there is plenty of scope for further improvement.

Combustion chamber requirements

Apart from the turbulence set up at the time of entry of the charge, it is required for maximum thermal efficiency that the agitation should continue right up to the moment of ignition. To this end, the free entry of gas, already dealt with, is the first consideration. Next, the combustion chamber should be devoid of nooks and crannies where stagnant gas may accumulate or become trapped. Finally, the agitation should be sufficient to keep on the move the layer of gas next to the cylinder walls, which will otherwise chill off and possibly escape complete burning.

The use of " squish," already described in the last chapter, is a quite effective way of ensuring continuance of turbulence, and is easily arranged on the popular o.h.v. type of engine having all valves in a row—the " bath-tub " formation of head. It is probable, however, that for consistency of turbulence (in regard to its persisting right through the inlet and succeeding phases up to the moment of ignition) the hemispherical shape is unsurpassed, its freedom from corners and odd shapes making no mean contribution to this result. There is, however, no gainsaying the fact that extremely high outputs are obtainable from the simpler " bath-tub " layout, and that this type has performed well in the past on relatively poor qualities of fuel, indicative of very good combustion characteristics.

Exhaust pressure

When considering the design of the inlet side of the engine we are up against the fact that all the time there is a limitation on the available pressure which can be used to push the mixture into the cylinder (assuming atmospheric induction). We are much better off when looking at the exhaust arrangements. Although we are accustomed to thinking of the last upstroke of the operating cycle as the exhaust stroke, it will be obvious that, at the time of exhaust valve opening, about 55 deg. or so before b.d.c., the cylinder will contain gas at a pressure of 60 or 70 lb. per sq. in. This pressure will ensure speedy evacuation of a large proportion of the exhaust gases before the commencement of the exhaust stroke proper. Further, with a cam formation giving the required quick opening characteristic, the sudden release of the pressure will start the rapid gas flow down the pipe which is required for good scavenge. The use of an unduly large valve and port may actually prejudice the scavenge effect without any compensating advantage which might be thought to arise from giving the outgoing gases an easier flow. The existing cylinder pressure is well able to look after the eviction process, even when the proportions of valve and port are such that the gas velocity through them is approaching 230 feet per second or so.

By the time the piston has passed b.d.c. practically the whole of the gases will be clear, and even if (for the sake of argument) the valve size is such that a back pressure of 1 lb. per sq. in. persisted throughout the exhaust stroke, this would represent a loss calculated on the b.m.e.p. of only the same amount. In fact, of course, the velocity of the outflow would be such that unless the valve were made outrageously small, no such pressure could build up.

A serious disadvantage of any exhaust valve is, of course, its large uncooled area. This used to be such a major snag that many designers went to considerable lengths to do away with it altogether, and substituted some other means of controlling the breathing—rotary or sleeve valves, for example. Cooling jacketing nowadays receives proper attention from designers, while spark plugs, which represent further uncooled areas, tend to become smaller, but the exhaust valve head still takes up considerable room. Obviously, therefore, the smaller it can be made the better, since not only will it pick up less heat, but it will more quickly dispose of such as it does unavoidably absorb.

Another point is, that the power required to open the valve against the cylinder pressure can be considerable, and this becomes greater with a large valve, throwing additional stresses on the operating mechanism. It is evident, therefore, that the fullest advantage is to be had by accepting as normal a gas speed through the exhaust valve of up to 50 per cent. greater than that permissible through the inlet valve. By so doing, we can reduce the size of the valve head to proportions which will keep its nuisance value as a hot-spot within bounds, and ensure that an unduly large amount of power is not absorbed in operating it.

If tuning operations are undertaken designed to push up the top end of the power curve, an increase in inlet valve size may be called for even at the expense of low-speed torque. In this event, the exhaust valve size might be advantageously increased also, but this is by no means a certainty, and it is the opinion of the writer that such experiments would be better conducted in two stages; first, enlargement of inlet valve only ; secondly, both valves.

Undue emphasis on sheer b.h.p. at peak revolutions can be most misleading, even in track-work, while for almost every other purpose a sensible torque curve, starting not too low down but reasonably so, is much to be preferred to a few revs gained, but seldom used, at the top end.

The influence of plug position

It has been suggested that good engine design should start with the spark plug, and certainly since this component is where the power stroke originates, the principle is not a bad one. Such factors as detonation and compression ratio are influenced to a large extent by plug position, the former being, of course, tied up with the amount of ignition advance which is permissible.

Since the plug must necessarily be inserted either into the top or the side of the combustion chamber, a position should be aimed at which will give as near as possible an equal distance from the combustion chamber wall in all directions.

For example, with an engine having hemispherical heads and inclined o.h.v., and forgetting the dictates of the latter for the moment, it might be feasible to have the plug vertically in the centre of the head. Such a position might be said to constitute almost the ideal, and although present-day valve sizes usually preclude the absolutely central position, most designers using hemispherically headed engines get as near to this location as possible.

It is, however, rather extraordinary that many designers are loth to take full advantage of reductions in plug size. The old 18-mm. thread took up an unacceptable amount of room, and the changeover to 14 mm., a diametric reduction amounting to 4 mm., of considerable value, took place very quickly. Plugs with 10-mm. threads have now been available for several years, representing a further 4 mm. of useful room, but so far their adoption in this country has been somewhat half-hearted. These dimensional reductions are most helpful in the plotting of combustion chamber layouts, and it is not difficult to see that with some modification to valves, and the use of the smallest possible plug, the central position for the latter could be achieved in a two-valve hemispherical head.

There is, however, another factor to be taken into consideration, and that is the desirability of ensuring adequate agitation of mixture in the neighbourhood of the plug, at the moment of ignition. It is possible that under conditions of varying throttle opening, with consequent variation of inlet mixture velocity, a plug position slightly to one side of the centre will be more likely to ensure a proper degree of swirl past the plug points. Nevertheless, the necessity for the shortest possible flame travel should receive first consideration. This problem is obviously more serious in large-bore engines, as with relatively small bores the dimensions are such that the plug can hardly ever be put in an impossibly bad position. When considering the claims made for " square " or big-bore engines it is instructive to realize that piston speed is not the only thing to be taken into account, and that such points as the above have also to receive attention.

In general, the shorter the flame travel the less sensitive will the engine be to throttle opening and load, in the matter of ignition timing control. The tendency towards detonation with inferior fuels will also be reduced. It has been suggested earlier that with careful design the makers of hemispherically headed engines can put the plug where they choose. In the case of the more popular type of head having the " bath-tub " shape, any suggestion of a central plug position is out of the question. The usual head of this type manages to accommodate two valves of adequate size in a most creditable manner, but there is certainly no room for anything else. A position for the plug must therefore be chosen at the side of the head. To counteract the long flame travel from this position across the piston crown we can fortunately arrange a " squish " formation almost directly opposite, so that in effect the mixture comes out to meet the plug just at the moment of ignition. As the " squish " areas are in addition almost in contact at t.d.c., this further reduces the combustion chamber dimensions as far as flame travel is concerned. Bore-stroke ratio again has some influence, as from the above point of view the smaller the cross-dimension of the head, the better.

In any form of combustion chamber, the use of a flat-top piston is desirable for efficient combustion. It is, of course, not always possible to obtain the required compression ratio with a perfectly flat crown, and this is another item where sensible compromise may be called for. Too much of a hump on the piston, however, may indicate that the bore and stroke dimensions have not been given sufficient consideration.

Ignition current

The importance of spark plug position has been considered at some length on an earlier page. It will now be useful to go further into the question of ignition current supply, and the type of plug. Whether magneto or coil system is employed for generation of the high-tension current, the latter is obtained initially from a low-voltage supply. In the case of the magneto, mechanical rotation of the armature is converted to l.t. current which is in turn transformed to h.t. within the armature winding. Thus, the magneto forms an entirely self-contained source of high-tension supply for the ignition.

In the case of coil ignition, the l.t. supply is obtained from the battery and the coil forms the transforming medium from which h.t. current is obtained. The coil system is thus dependent on the main electrical system. The fundamental difference between the two systems is, of course, that in the case of the magneto, the spark strength increases as the speed rises, whereas a fixed voltage is applied in the coil system. The latter is advantageous at starting, as it is independent of engine cranking speed and it has no apparent disadvantage at the highest speeds obtainable under racing conditions.

Control of the ignition point on modern engines is usually automatic, by means of a centrifugal device which operates according to engine r.p.m. This is a simple and effective method, but does not take into account a second factor calling for timing variation, namely, the density of mixture, or throttle opening. In order to exercise control over this condition, a second device is frequently introduced, comprising a diaphragm operated by induction manifold vacuum. This is arranged to advance the spark timing when manifold pressure is high, and to retard it under the opposite condition. In conjunction with the centrifugal control, virtually all conditions of engine operation are covered.

There is still considerable advantage in having a hand-operated control which overrides the automatic device or devices, if only to compensate for different grades of fuel, carbon deposits, engine temperature, and so on, none of these conditions being catered for by any automatic mechanism.

Coils and plugs

High performance coils are frequently recommended for use on high-efficiency engines. These differ from the normal type in having a superior class of insulation, and usually a higher h.t. voltage, thus enabling larger plug gaps to be used.

It is of interest to consider that thirty or more years ago, a plug gap of about .012 in. was customary, the plug having 18-mm. thread. Nowadays, plugs with a thread diameter of 14 or 10 mm. are commonplace, using a gap of up to .030 in. This speaks volumes for the quality of the insulation used, and obviously the reduction in overall size of the plug is of great advantage in combustion chamber design.

In high-speed engines, where it is necessary to ensure that plenty of oil reaches the upper parts of the cylinder bores, there may be occasions when an excess of oil is present in the combustion chamber itself. Such engines require plugs capable of burning off excess oil, without becoming incandescent and causing pre-ignition under full-throttle operation.

It has been found that plugs with comparatively thin electrodes maintain a fairly constant temperature irrespective of the amount of throttle opening, whilst plugs with heavier electrodes undergo considerable temperature variations, depending on whether the engine is on light or open throttle. It will be evident from this, that the latter type of plug may be a cure for pre-ignition at full throttle, but will have a marked tendency to oil up when the temperature drops, at lower speeds.

It does not necessarily follow, therefore, that because the engine is of a high-output design, it requires a racing plug with massive points. In many cases, experiment will show which is the most satisfactory type. In this connection, it is better to commence with a plug having light electrodes and a tendency to pre-ignite, and to work from this point, rather than to begin with a heavy, " oily " plug. It is, in other words, much easier to cure pre-ignition than oiling-up, and fewer plug changes will be necessary than would be the case when starting at the " pre-ignition " end of the scale.

H

CHAPTER 8

A High-Grade Design—The Aston Martin

Power output—The crankshaft assembly—Cylinder head and valve gear—
The lubrication system—The cooling system

Power output

The Aston Martin power unit is fully representative of the sports-car engine of high-grade design and manufacture. It is one of the comparatively few British engines with double overhead camshafts, and it is natural that the valve gear arrangement should be one of the first items to attract the attention of those looking for " performance" features. Actually, however, it is in the crankshaft and main bearing arrangement that this engine shows considerable originality of layout.

The engine, of six cylinders, measures 78 by 90 mm., giving a swept volume of 2,580 c.c. The normal output for touring-car purposes is 107 b.h.p. at 5,000 r.p.m., using a comp. r. of 6.5 : 1, and corresponding to a maximum torque of 130 lb. ft. at 3,000 r.p.m. The competition " Vantage " engine, with comp. r. of 8.16 : 1, develops 123 b.h.p. at 5,000 r.p.m., the maximum torque of 144 lb. ft. being obtained at 2,400 r.p.m.

The crankshaft assembly

The crankshaft layout having already been mentioned as an interesting feature, this will be described first. The crank-case and cylinder block comprise a single iron casting, the former being of box formation, with the front main bearing housing integral therewith. To carry the remaining three bearings, however, circular machined housings are provided in the casting, and into these, split bearing carriers of light alloy are assembled. These bearing carriers are, of course, first fitted in position on the shaft which is then threaded into the crankcase from the back end.

It will be obvious that this construction allows the circular housings in the main casting to be very substantially supported by ribbing, as will be seen from the illustrations on page 84. It would appear, on the other hand, that the fit of the alloy bearing carriers in their annular machined registers must be to extremely close limits if the fullest advantage is to be taken of the rigidity of the main casting. The alloy bearing carriers are located, after insertion, by setscrews from below, which mate with slots in the carriers.

Glacier steel-backed white-metal bearings are carried by the aluminium split carriers, the two carrier-halves being united by three bolts, two on one side (one on either side of the oil-feed pipe) and one on the other. The carriers are 6 in. diameter outside, while the shaft journal diameter is 2.5 in., giving exceptional rigidity. The front main bearing (carried, as mentioned earlier, in the main casting) is of the full sleeve type, the steel sleeve being white-metal lined. Thrust rings are provided on the end faces of this bearing to give axial crankshaft location.

The cylinder liners are of the centrifugally cast type, in direct contact with the cooling water, and flanged for sealing at the lower ends. Figure-eight sealing washers are used at this point for each pair of cylinders. With the cylinder head off, the liners protrude from the block a matter of .005 in. or so, the fitting of the head thus holding the liners firmly down and completing the seal at both ends.

The crankshaft is of case-hardening steel with integral counterweights, and crankpins of 2 in. diameter. It is drilled in the normal manner for bearing lubrication. The driving sleeve at the front end carries two duplex chain pinions and the fan pulley, Woodruff keys giving the necessary location, and a nut holding the assembly firmly. The aluminium timing housing carries an oil-resisting rubber seal at the front end, while a return thread is turned on the outside of the flywheel flange at the rear end, together with a thrower ring.

The connecting rods are of steel, with ample ribbing at the big-ends, and are of the usual H-section. The big-end studs are formed in one piece with the rod, and are a dead fit in the bearing cap, which is thus located accurately. The big-end

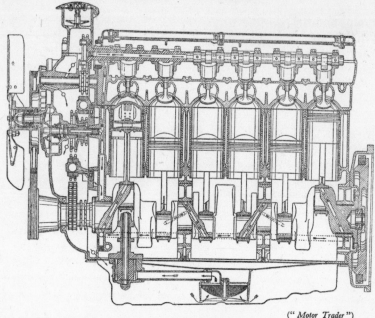

("*Motor Trader*")

GENERAL ARRANGEMENT OF ASTON MARTIN D.B.2 ENGINE. BORE AND
STROKE 78 MM. & 90 MM.

bearings are white-metalled direct on the rod and cap, the
components naturally being bored in unit before metalling.
The small-end bearing is of phosphor-bronze.

The pistons are straightforward solid-skirt type of either
Hepworth and Grandage or Specialloid make, and they each
have two compression and two slotted oil-control rings.

Cylinder head and valve gear

The cylinder head is of chromium iron, held down by
fourteen studs. The combustion chambers are of hemispherical formation, the valves being at an included angle of
60 deg. An interesting point regarding the valves is that the
seat angle of the inlets is 30 deg. and that of the exhausts 45 deg.
The inlet valve is larger than the exhaust, a feature which is
usual in high-output engines. The respective dimensions are
1.515 in. and 1.375 in. In each case the lift is 11/32 in.

The valves are operated through short tappets of the
thimble type, giving a very direct form of attack with the

minimum of reciprocating weight. There is no provision for quick adjustment of tappet-to-valve clearance, this being adjusted initially (and subsequently as required) by selective assembly, the boss on the inside of the thimble, which contacts the valve-stem, being ground in a variety of thicknesses to allow of this being done. The thimbles have their bearing direct in the iron head, as also do the camshafts, which latter are of Monikrom chill-cast material. The extremely rigid nature of the camshaft bearing arrangement will be evident from a study of the sectional drawing of the engine on page 118.

The two camshafts are driven by a two-stage Renold chain drive. For initial camshaft timing, each of the camshaft

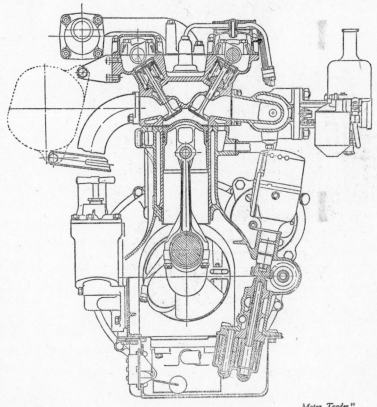

Motor Trader "

CROSS-SECTION OF ASTON MARTIN DB2 ENGINE

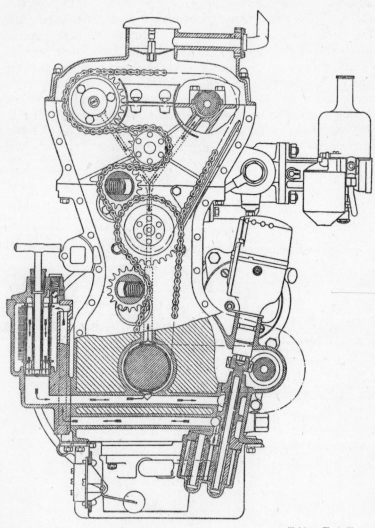

("*Motor Trader*")

CAMSHAFT DRIVE AND OIL CIRCULATION SYSTEM

chainwheels has nine small holes in its flange. After timing, the selected hole is bored out, to fit a setscrew which registers with a corresponding hole in the camshaft flange. Two further setscrews, but of different diameter, complete the assembly. By this means, no subsequent dismantling will cause the original relationship of the chainwheel to the cam-shaft to be lost.

The intermediate spindle of the two-stage chain drive serves to drive the water-pump, the housing of which is formed as part of the timing cover. The idler wheel between the two camshafts is, as will be seen from the illustration on page 85, carried on a very substantial shaft and bearings, which seems to indicate an initial intention to utilize this point as a cooling fan drive. (The fan is, however, driven by vee-belt from the crankshaft.) Each stage of the chain drive is provided with a tensioning jockey of Aston Martin design, hydraulically loaded from the engine lubrication system, and the chain is of the duplex roller type, with a pitch measure-ment of .375 in. The valve timing is as follows:—

Inlet opens 9.5 deg. before t.d.c.; closes 74.5 deg. after b.d.c.

Exhaust opens 51.5 deg. before b.d.c. ; closes 33.5 deg. after t.d.c.

Overlap 43 deg.

The lubrication system

On the nearside of the engine there is a shaft, driven from the crankshaft by a 1 : 1 ratio duplex roller chain drive. This shaft carries a skew gear which drives the gear-type oil pump and ignition distributor. The pump draws from the alloy sump via a strainer of the normal gauze type, and delivers to an Auto-Klean filter mounted on the engine off-side. From the filter, the oil is pressure-fed through a cross-gallery at the front of the engine, to the main oil gallery along the engine nearside. The main gallery feeds the intermediate and rear crankshaft bearings, while the front bearing is served from the cross-gallery via an annular groove behind the bearing. From this annular groove a vertical passage leads through a pressure-restrictor plug to the cylinder head oil passages which feed the front camshaft bearings. The camshafts are drilled axially, the oil passing thereto by means of oilways drilled radially in the front thrust flanges as shown in the illustration on page 116. Radial drillways supply all the camshaft bearings, while drilled plugs inserted in the front ends of the camshaft axial oilways, allow a metered flow of lubricant to drain down over the chain and the upper idler spindle. Tappings from the vertical feed duct (already mentioned as feeding the cylinder head) lubricate the chain tensioners and the water-pump spindle. The normal oil pressure is about 80 lb. per sq. in. at 4,500 r.p.m.

The cooling system

A water manifold is provided along the cylinder block off-side, to which the water-pump delivers. From the manifold, there are three ducts to the cylinder jackets. After passing over the cylinder liners, the water goes to the induction manifold jackets on the engine nearside, and up to the cylinder head via suitable holes. In the cylinder block top face, adjacent to the liner flanges there are air-pocket relief holes through which water can pass to the exhaust valve guides, the flow being specifically directed to these points.

The outlet from the cylinder head leads to the header tank or, under thermostat control, to the pump inlet by-pass, the thermostat operating at a temperature of about 85 deg. C.

The two S.U. carburetters, normally type H4, feed cylinders 1–2–3 and 4–5–6 respectively, via cast light alloy jacketed manifolds, a balance pipe connecting the branches. A starter carburetter of thermostatic type feeds into the balance pipe.

A Lucas coil and distributor is used, and this engine is one of the relatively few fitting 10-mm. plugs, these being (normally) K.L.G. make with .022 in. gap.

CHAPTER 9

Power per c.c.—The Bristol

High output—The crankcase assembly—Connecting rods and pistons—
Camshaft and valve gear—The cylinder head—The lubrication and cooling
systems—Further developments

High output

The two-litre Bristol engine can be said to incorporate all that is best in engine design, while retaining sufficient originality to warrant a good deal of close investigation. The first thing to be noted is that the output of even the most " touring " version of the power unit is on a par with the best motor-cycle engines in terms of b.h.p. per unit of cubic capacity—and this is by no means usual in car engines. In supertuned form, as developed by the famous Frazer-Nash concern, outputs in the order of 75 b.h.p. per litre are reliably obtained.

Powering cars variously referred to by type numbers 400, 401 and 402, four types of Bristol engine had been produced until recently, when a modified unit, type 100A, was introduced for the car type 403. Of the four original types, the 85 had a single twin-choke Solex carburetter. This engine was replaced by type 85A having three S.U. carburetters. Type 85B, produced to special order, is similar to 85A with the exception of a modified camshaft and other small changes, while 85C has three Solex carburetters. The power outputs of the engines are as follows:—

Type	B.h.p.	R.p.m.	Max. torque (lb. ft.)	R.p.m.
85A	80	4,200	102	3,000
85B	90	4,500	102	3,500
85C	85	4,500	106	3,500
100A	100	5,250	110	3,500

The general design of all types is similar, see illustrations on pages 86 and 87, and sectional arrangement, page 122.

(" Motor Trader ")

Longitudinal and transverse engine sections. Alternative car-burettors shown

SECTION OF THE BRISTOL ENGINE

The crankcase assembly

The cast-iron crankcase and cylinder block forms a unit, with dry liners for the bores in the later types. The crankshaft is carried on four main bearings of the thin-wall steel-backed lead bronze type with tab location. Split thrust washers on either side of the front bearing control the shaft end-float. The main bearing housings are of the normal type with caps located by two studs.

The crankshaft is nitrided, and thus grinding is not possible without subsequent re-nitriding. Main bearings on engines prior to the type 100A are 2 in. diameter, and crankpins 1.77 in. (The type 100A has larger bearings.) The length

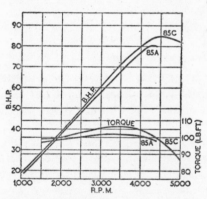

PERFORMANCE GRAPH OF THE 2-LITRE
BRISTOL ENGINE

of bearings 1 and 4 is 1.25 in. and of 2 and 3, 1 in. The timing chain pinion and thrust plate is keyed on the fore end of the shaft by a Woodruff key, while the fan and dynamo pulley is also fitted with a separate key, an oil thrower ring being positioned between the chain pinion and the pulley. The pulley hub passes through a felt sealing ring located in a groove in the timing chain cover. The assembly of pulley, pinion, etc., is retained by the starting handle dog-nut. An oscillation damper of the bonded-rubber type is integral with the pulley.

At the rear end of the crankshaft, the flywheel is spigoted to a flange and retained by six setscrews and a dowel. A spring ring in its centre holds the ball-bearing of the clutch-shaft spigot. The starter gear-ring, with 108/9 teeth, is shrunk on to the wheel.

Connecting rods and pistons

The big-ends of the connecting rods are of the thin-wall steel-backed lead-bronze type, tab-located. The gudgeon pins are fully floating, bronze bushes being provided in the small-ends. The rods are drilled for pressure oil-feed to the bushes.

The pistons are of aluminium alloy, tin-plated, with slightly domed crowns. The skirts are solid, oval-machined and tapered. Circlips retain the floating gudgeon pins. There are four piston rings, all above the pin, the top ring being chromium plated. The next two rings are respectively plain and tapered, while the bottom one is a slotted oil-control type.

Camshaft and valve gear

The single camshaft is located in the crankcase, and driven by duplex Renold roller chain without any tensioning device. The shaft runs in four plain bronze sleeve bearings, the chain-wheel being Woodruff-keyed on the front end, with a thrust plate between the chainwheel and the shoulder of the front bearing. A skew gear is provided for the distributor and oil-pump drive. The camshaft operates barrel tappets sliding directly in the crankcase. The cylinder head carries two rocker-shafts, the inlet rockers, on the nearside, being operated direct by push-rods from the camshaft. The exhaust rockers on the offside are operated by short push-rods across the head from bell-crank levers carried on the inlet rocker-shaft and receiving motion from vertical push-rods in the normal way. (See page 56.)

The push-rods are of different types, depending on their duty. The inlet push-rods have the usual ball-end at the bottom, and cup-end at the top for receiving the adjustment screw in the rocker-end. The exhaust push-rods have a ball at each end, the adjustment in this case being obtained on the short transverse push-rods which have a ball at the bell-crank lever end, and a cup at the exhaust rocker-end.

The valves are non-interchangeable, the inlets being 1.425 in. diameter and the exhausts 1.31 in. (this applying to engines other than type 100A). The face angle in each case is 45 deg. Double valve springs are used, and the valve guides are of plain bronze. Hardened valve seats are shrunk into the light alloy cylinder head. The valve timing is as follows:—

Engines type 85, 85A, 85C:
>   Inlet opens 10 deg. before t.d.c.; closes 50 deg. after b.d.c.
>   Exhaust opens 50 deg. before b.d.c.; closes 10 deg. after t.d.c.
>   Overlap 20 deg.

Engine type 85B:
>   Inlet opens 40 deg. before t.d.c.; closes 80 deg. after b.d.c.
>   Exhaust opens 80 deg. before b.d.c.; closes 40 deg. after t.d.c.
>   Overlap 80 deg.

Engine type 100A:
>   Inlet opens 15 deg. before t.d.c.; closes 65 deg. after b.d.c.
>   Exhaust opens 65 deg. before b.d.c.; closes 15 deg. after t.d.c.
>   Overlap 30 deg.

The cylinder head

The alloy cylinder head has hemispherical combustion chambers, and is held down by fourteen studs. Six exhaust ports emerge from the offside, all the ports being separate. The inlet ports are paired 1–2, 3–4, and 5–6, and coupled in that manner to the three carburetters, the ports facing vertically upwards. This provides true down-draft carburation with a remarkably free gravity-assisted intake to the inlet valves. The form of inlet porting is, of course, facilitated by the use of transverse push-rods for exhaust-valve operation, as the method leaves the centre of the head very free of obstruction. The 10-mm. spark plugs are mounted centrally in the combustion chambers.

The lubrication and cooling systems

The oil-pump is of the normal gear type, flange-mounted in the bottom of the crankcase, and driven from the camshaft by a loose quill from the skew gear, which runs in a bronze bush. The same gears drive the distributor. The pump is fitted with a gauze intake strainer, the delivery taking place through the pump body via a drilling in the crankcase wall to an external full-flow filter of Tecalemit or Vokes type. From the filter outlet, the oil passes through drillings to the main and camshaft bearings, and to each rocker-shaft. (A U-pipe carries the oil from the block to the head to feed the rocker-shafts.)

On early engines, an oil-to-water heat exchanger was mounted in a tunnel on the crankcase offside. This was discontinued, the connections being blanked off. Provision is now made for fitting an external oil-radiator. Pressure relief is provided by a spring-loaded plunger-type valve on the near-side of the crankcase, the valve being adjustable by screw-driver after removing a cap-nut above the filter. The normal pressure is 60 lb. per sq. in. with oil and water temperatures of 70 deg. C., and r.p.m. of 3,000. The water-pump is of the centrifugal impeller type with sealing arrangement depending on engine type. The pump is driven by vee-belt in conjunction with the dynamo, and the fan is mounted on an extension of the pump shaft.

Six setscrews hold the pump body to the front of the cylinder head. The radiator is fitted with thermostatically controlled shutters. The ignition distributor is arranged for clockwise rotation, and has centrifugally controlled automatic advance mechanism. A hand control, over-riding the automatic device, is a valuable feature. The distributor body is spigot-mounted in the crankcase, and its drive shaft engages the oil-pump drive. A skew gear for the tachometer drive is incorporated in the lower end of the body, and there is an oil-feed to here from the main oil gallery.

Further developments

In October, 1953, the Company announced further high-speed models, using engines of similar type to the 100A, but having the compression ratio raised to 8.5 : 1. With valve timing as on the 100A, the new type 100B unit develops 105 b.h.p. at 5,000 r.p.m. Alternatively it is obtainable with valve timing as used on the type 85B, when an output of 125 b.h.p. is developed at 5,500 r.p.m. This latter engine would normally be employed for high-speed competition work only, and is designated 100C. The 100B engine is illustrated on page 86.

CHAPTER 10

Rugged Simplicity—The Ford

The " Prefect "—Crankcase assembly—Connecting rods and pistons—Valve gear—
The lubrication system—The ignition system—The " Consul " and " Zephyr "—
Crankshaft assembly—Connecting rods and pistons—Cylinder head and valve gear—
Lubrication and cooling systems

The " Prefect "

No book dealing with the design of competition car engines would be complete without reference to what is the most successful " trials " engine of the day, as far as events for " specials " are concerned—the Ford Prefect. In contrast to other types of engine dealt with in these pages, the Ford is the embodiment of stark simplicity. Therein lies much of its appeal, and it must be emphasized that careful attention to the correct functioning of the relatively few components will pay dividends in increased performance out of all proportion to the modest character of the power unit.

The four-cylinder engine has a bore and stroke of 63.5 by 92.5 mm., giving a swept volume of 1,172 c.c. At the comfortably modest r.p.m. of 4,000, 30 b.h.p. is claimed, with a maximum torque of 46.4 lb. ft. at 2,400 r.p.m., all with comp. r. of 6.16 : 1. The smaller Anglia engine, of almost identical design, has the bore reduced to 56.64 mm., giving a swept volume of 933 c.c., but this is naturally rarely used for competition work.

The simplicity of the layout is well shown by the sectional drawings on page 129. A single iron casting forms the crankcase and cylinder block, and since side-by-side valves are used, the valve ports and seatings are also formed therein.

The crankcase assembly

The crankshaft, of special cast material, is carried in three main bearings of the thin-wall steel-backed type with white-

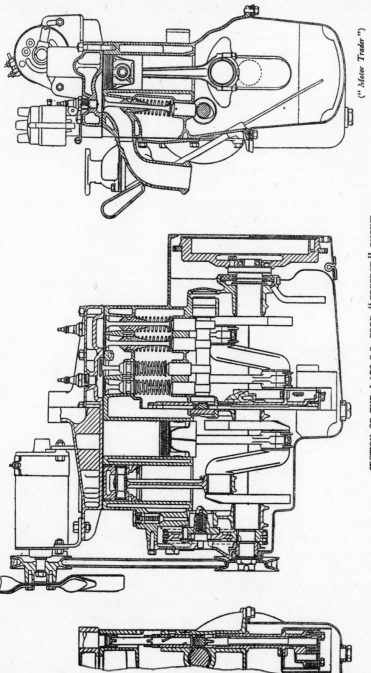

("Motor Trader")

SECTION OF THE 1,172-C.C. FORD "PREFECT" ENGINE

metal linings, having tab location in the split housings. End thrust is taken on the rear bearing, which is flanged for this purpose. Each bearing cap is retained by two bolts. The journals are of large diameter, $1\frac{5}{8}$ in., the respective lengths being: front, $1\frac{5}{8}$ in.; centre, 1 5/16 in.; rear, 2 in. A flange at the rear carries the flywheel, which is spigot-mounted thereon, and secured by four setscrews and two dowels. Two oil-thrower flanges are cast on the shaft in front of the fly-wheel flange, and these run inside a die-cast grooved housing having an oil-drain pipe leading into the bottom of the sump. The rear wall of the sump has a soft packing around the bearing housing to complete the joint.

At the front, the timing chain pinion is secured by a Woodruff key, and has an oil-thrower disc between it and the fan pulley, which latter is a press-fit on the shaft and outside the timing chain cover. The starting handle dog, screwed into the shaft end, secures all these components. A com-position packing ring, located in the timing chain cover and the sump, between the oil thrower and fan pulley, looks after the oil retention at this point.

Connecting rods and pistons

The steel connecting rods are metalled direct with a white-metal lining at the big-ends, the small-ends being bronze-bushed. The big-end journals are $1\frac{1}{2}$ in. diameter with a length of 13/16 in. The rod eyes are split at right-angles to the axis of the rod, the big-end caps being retained by two bolts each.

Aluminium alloy split-skirt pistons are used, with fully floating gudgeon pins retained by circlips. Two compression and one oil-control ring are fitted, all located above the gudgeon pin.

The cylinder head is of cast-iron, with the bulk of the clearance space above the valves, and a flat area to promote " squish " above the piston. The spark plug bosses are located almost directly above the valves. The head is held down by no less than thirteen studs—a good point. Ample water spaces are provided, with a central take-off to the radiator header tank.

The valve gear

The camshaft runs in three bearings directly in the crank-case, without linings. Its end-float is controlled by means of a spring-loaded plunger fitted into the shaft at the chain-wheel end, and bearing against a thrust pad inside the chain-case. A bronze thrust ring is provided between the chain-wheel and the end bearing.

The shaft is driven from the crankshaft by a Renold .375 in. pitch duplex roller chain, without any tensioning device. The chainwheel is held on the camshaft by a spigot fitting, three setscrews and two dowels. The tappets are of the cylindrical type, bearing direct in the crankcase. The valves are non-adjustable, having wide-based stems bearing on the tappets. Initial adjustment for correct clearance is obtained by grinding the stems. The valve guides are split, the upward pressure of the valve springs retaining them in the block. One spring only per valve is used, retained by a horseshoe collar. The valves are all of the same size, having a head diameter of 1 7/64 in. Inlets and exhausts are, however, of different materials. The face angle is 45 deg. The valve timing is as follows:—

Inlet opens 9.5 deg. before t.d.c.; closes 50.5 deg. after b.d.c.

Exhaust opens 53.5 deg. before b.d.c.; closes 6.5 deg. after t.d.c.

Overlap 16 deg.

Four separate exhaust ports are provided, and two siamesed inlet ports.

The lubrication system

A gear-type oil-pump is skew-gear driven from the cam-shaft by means of a short shaft having dogs at each end for driving the pump and distributor. The pump is mounted low down in the sump, and has a gauze suction filter surround-ing it. The oil delivery takes place via the hollow drive housing to an open-sided gallery which is enclosed by the tappet cover when the latter is in position. From the gallery, drillings lead to the main bearings, and the crankshaft is drilled for big-end lubrication. A by-pass filter is provided, connected to a union at the front of the gallery. The oil-pressure relief valve maintains a pressure of about 30 lb. per sq. in. It is of the non-adjustable spring-loaded plunger type, fitted at the front of the crankcase above the timing drive, and can be seen clearly in the sectional drawing on page 129.

The ignition system

The distributor is driven from a vertical shaft incorporated in the oil-pump drive, and is mounted high up on the nearside of the block. It has centrifugal advance and retard mechanism, while further adjustment of timing is facilitated by a slotted plate clamped by a setscrew. The timing range given by the automatic mechanism is 20 deg. The standard spark plugs are Champion type C, 14-mm. thread.

The cooling water circulation is by natural flow, no pump being fitted. The fan is mounted on the dynamo spindle, the latter being carried on a bracket on the cylinder head. Belt drive is employed to the dynamo and fan, belt tension being adjusted by swinging the dynamo on its bracket.

Towards the end of 1953, various modifications were made to the standard engine aimed at increased power output, without departing from the same well-tried layout. It is in the basic form described, however, that the engine is best known to competition enthusiasts.

The Ford " Consul " and " Zephyr "

Although of comparatively recent origin, the Ford o.h.v. in-line engines designated as above are already being fitted to one prominent make of British sports car, and there is little doubt that many potential builders will have one or other of these units in mind, in view of the success of the smaller side-valve types in all classes of competition work. The two sizes of o.h.v. engine are of very similar design, one having four cylinders and the other six. Bore and stroke in each case

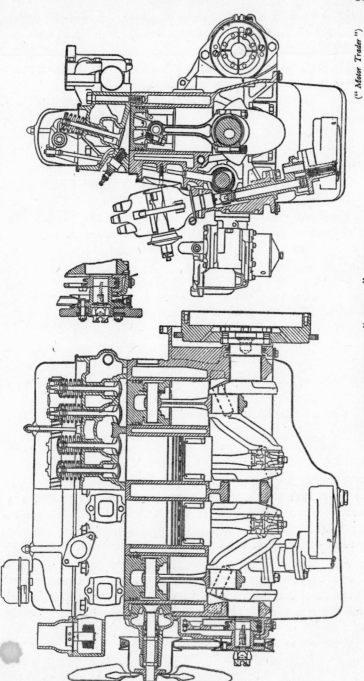

("*Motor Trader*")

SECTION OF THE FORD "CONSUL" ENGINE

is 79.37 by 76.2 mm., giving a swept volume for the Consul four-cylinder of 1,508 c.c., and for the Zephyr, six of 2,262 c.c.

The Consul develops 47 b.h.p. at 4,400 r.p.m., with a maximum torque of 74 lb. ft. at 2,400 r.p.m.   This corresponds to a b.m.e.p. of 121 lb. per sq. in.   The Zephyr has an output of 68 b.h.p. at 4,000 r.p.m., maximum torque being 112 lb. ft. at 2,000 r.p.m., and b.m.e.p. 122 lb. per sq. in.   In each case a comp. r. of 6.8 : 1 is used.   (See illustrations, page 89–90.)

The crankshaft assembly

The crankcase and cylinder block assemblies of the two engines are of similar design, the Consul having three main bearings and the Zephyr four.   The face of the sump joint is considerably below the centre-line of the shaft, as is clearly shown in the sectional drawing on page 135.   The main bearing caps are of cast-iron, each being secured by two 7/16-in. setscrews.   For axial location of the crankshaft, the centre bearing on the four-cylinder engine carries white-metalled shims on either side; the same method is used on the six, the shims in this case being on number three bearing.

The shaft is cast in the special material developed by the Ford Company, and is counterweighted on each crank-throw. The main bearings comprise white-metal steel-backed thin-wall liners.   The big-ends are of similar construction.

The main bearing journals are 2.25 in. diameter, the length being 1 in. for the front, 1.5 in. for the rear, and 1.25 in. for intermediates.   The crankpins, which are drilled for light-ness, have a diameter of 1.937 in. and a length of 1.125 in.

A flange for the flywheel is integral with the rear end of the shaft, the flywheel being secured thereon by four set-screws with a locking plate, and a dowel.   An oil return groove between the flange and the rear main bearing operates in conjunction with a split composition oil-sealing ring.

The camshaft drive-chain pinion, and fan pulley, are secured on the front of the shaft by a single Woodruff key. No starter dog is fitted, but a setscrew and washer at the front locks the assembly.   There is a lipped oil-seal in the timing chain cover, in which the pulley hub runs to ensure retention of lubricant at this point.

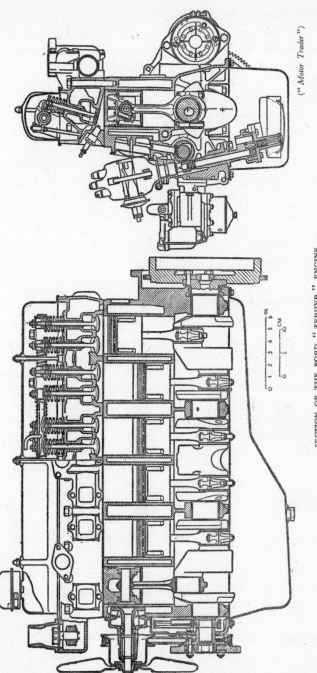

("Motor Trader")

SECTION OF THE FORD "ZEPHYR" ENGINE

Connecting rods and pistons

The connecting rods are of alloy steel, the big-end caps being secured by two bolts with locking nuts. The small-ends of the rods are split and clamp-nutted to secure the gudgeon pins, the latter being 13/16 in. diameter.

The pistons are of aluminium alloy with solid skirts, and incorporate steel struts. Two compression and one oil oil-control ring are fitted, all above the gudgeon pin, the former having stepped upper faces providing some scraper effect. An interesting feature is the offsetting of the crankshaft and gudgeon pin centres, the axes of which are " in front " of a vertical line through the cylinder bores to the extent of .0625 in. This feature is claimed to reduce piston slap at t.d.c. (which is sometimes caused by rock as the piston changes over) and to equalize the bearing-surface pressure on the piston skirt due to connecting rod angularity.

The cylinder head and valve gear

The detachable iron cylinder head is secured by twelve and seventeen studs in the four and the six respectively. The head joint is formed by a bright steel gasket having raised ribs at all sealing points. The gasket is coated with synthetic varnish to complete the seal. The combustion chambers have their " squish " areas at back and front, and not opposite the spark plugs. Reference to the sectional view on page 135 will show how the simple shape gives a 14-deg. inclination to the top of the chamber, and also to the valve stems. The spark plugs are fitted into the deepest part of the head.

The valves have a head diameter of 1.437 and 1.187 in. respectively for inlet and exhaust, the face angle in each case being 45 deg. Lift is .35 in. A notable feature is in the exhaust valves which have heads and stems of different grades of steel welded together.

A single spring is used on each valve, the lower three or so turns being very closely pitched with the object of damping out surge by contact.

The rocker-shaft is of carbon steel, the rockers being malleable iron, phosphate-coated on the bearing surfaces.

The usual rocker adjustment is provided at the push-rod ends. The valve timing is as follows:—

Inlet opens 17 deg. before t.d.c.; closes 51 deg. after b.d.c.

Exhaust opens 40 deg. before b.d.c.; closes 19 deg. after t.d.c.

Overlap 36 deg.

The camshaft is of nickel chrome steel, running in steel-backed bearings (three for the Consul and four for the Zephyr). It is driven by a Renold duplex roller chain of .375 in. pitch, without a tensioning device. Positive lubrication is provided to the chain drive by a jet feed from the front camshaft bearing. The camshaft chainwheel is spigoted on the shaft end, and retained by two setscrews having a locking plate, and a dowel. Axial location is catered for by a bronze fork running in a groove at the driving end of the shaft. The tappets are of mushroom formation and take their bearing directly in the crankcase casting.

The lubrication and cooling systems

The normal type of gear oil-pump is mounted low down in the pressed-steel sump, and driven by skew gears from the camshaft. An upward extension of the drive looks after the ignition distributor. A gauze strainer is provided on the intake to the pump, and the pressure delivery is to a full-flow filter on the outside of the crankcase, offside. From the filter the oil is fed to the main gallery, which has drillings to main and camshaft bearings, and a pipe to the rocker-shaft and valve gear. The filter relief valve is in the filter cover, while the pump relief valve is of the plunger type, non-adjustable, and housed in the pump body. The normal pressure is 50 to 60 lb. per sq. in.

The ignition distributor is controlled by vacuum and centrifugal mechanism, and is driven by shaft and dogs from the oil-pump drive. The standard spark plugs are Champion type NA8, with 14-mm. thread.

The water pump is mounted in the front of the cylinder water jacket, and driven by vee-belt from the crankshaft. The cooling fan is also mounted on the pump spindle which has ball bearings and a carbon ring sealing gland. The pump draws from the bottom of the radiator and delivers to the cylinder jackets, the water outlet being from the front of the head, and incorporating a bellows-type thermostat. The whole cooling system is pressurized at 4 lb. per sq. in.

The exhaust manifold comprises a simple steel pipe with ports cut in the side to register with the cylinder ports. The pipe is retained by clamps, as shown in the view of the head on page 88. The induction manifold is of aluminium alloy and has a central lug cast thereon to conduct heat from the exhaust pipe and serve as a hot-spot. This lug acts as one of the clamps. A two-branch induction manifold is used on the Consul, and a three-branch on the Zephyr. Ribs are cast internally in the latter type, to assist mixture distribution. Separate exhaust ports are provided for each cylinder, while the inlet ports are siamesed. A single carburetter is used, of the Zenith down-draught type.

CHAPTER 11

Classic Layout—The Jaguar

Power output—The crankcase assembly—Cylinder head and valve gear—
Auxiliary drives—The cooling system

Power output

It is no exaggeration to state that, of the larger sports car engines, the $3\frac{1}{2}$ litre type XK120 Jaguar unit is the best known in the world. It has made available to the enthusiast, at a competitive price, features which have been accepted as belonging more to the exclusive era of Grand Prix engines of thirty years ago—the time of robustly constructed big-capacity engines with twin overhead camshafts and a multiplicity of main bearings. The construction of this engine is such that the already high power output can be augmented to a large degree without affecting reliability.

The six cylinders have a bore and stroke of 83 by 106 mm., the swept volume being 3,442 c.c. With a comp. r. of 8 : 1, 160 b.h.p. is developed at 5,200 r.p.m. Torque and b.m.e.p. readings are at maximum at 2,500 r.p.m., being 195 lb. ft. and 140 lb. per sq. in. respectively.

The crankcase assembly

The cylinder block and crankcase form a single chrome-iron casting of very robust construction, the housings for the seven main crankshaft bearings being well ribbed and filleted. Water spaces are provided between all cylinders, the bores of the latter being hone-finished. No cylinder liners are used.

The main bearing caps are held by two bolts and registered accurately by two dowels. The bearings themselves are of the Vandervell thin-wall steel-backed type having two oil-feed holes in each half-shell. The pressure oil supply is taken to the bearings via a drilled longitudinal gallery and cross-drillings to individual bearings. The central bearing is faced with white metal to take crankshaft end-thrust.

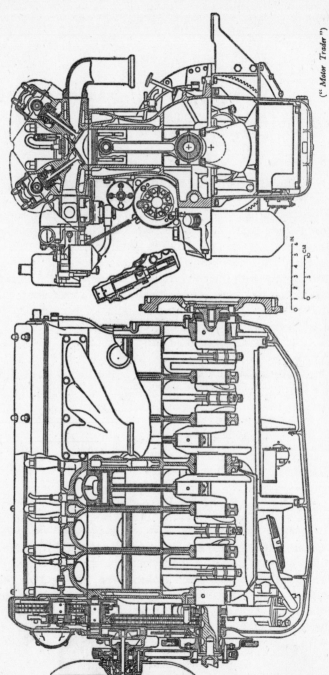

("Motor Trader")

SECTION OF THE 3·5-LITRE JAGUAR XK120 ENGINE

The crankshaft is of manganese molybdenum steel, the main journal diameters being 2.75 in. and the crankpins 2.088 in. The rear of the shaft terminates in a flywheel attachment flange, before which is an oil thrower and return thread. The housing for the return thread is formed in two halves, in the cylinder block casting and sump respectively. At the front end, the shaft carries a skew gear and duplex chain pinion for the various drive take-offs, and also a vibration damper of the Metalastik bonded-rubber type. Woodruff keys secure all these items, end location being provided by the starting-handle dog-bolt and washer screwed into the shaft end. The front oil seal comprises a thrower disc and a graphited asbestos ring housed in the end casting.

The crankshaft is drilled for big-end lubrication. A feature of the drilling, which is shown on the illustration on page 140, is the very large diameter blind hole drilled diagonally in each crankpin, which feeds the journal via the smaller holes. It will be evident that the " dead " end of the larger hole will form a very effective trap for foreign matter without prejudicing the flow to the big-end.

The steel connecting rods have Vandervell thin-wall steel-backed bearings at the big-ends. The caps are held by two fitted bolts. A positive oil-feed is taken to the small-end by a 3/16 in. diameter drilling up the centre of the rod.

The aluminium alloy pistons are of Aerolite make with solid skirts and having two compression and one scraper ring, all above the gudgeon pin. The pistons are tin-plated and the upper compression ring is chromium-plated. The gudgeon pins are fully floating, and retained by circlips.

The cylinder head and valve gear

The cylinder head is of RR50 aluminium alloy, and is held by fourteen main studs. There are also six further studs surrounding the camshaft drive housing at the front, as shown in the illustration on page 90. The combustion chambers are hemispherical, while the porting has received very careful attention in regard to promoting the maximum turbulence, the inlet ports being distinctly offset in plan, and curved to give a swirl effect.

The valves are arranged at an included angle of 70 deg. and seat on shrunk-in inserts, the seat angles being 30 deg. inlet and 45 deg. exhaust. Valve head diameters for inlet and exhaust are 1.75 in. and 1.438 in. respectively, the lift in each case being .313 in. The timing is as follows :—

Inlet opens 15 deg. before t.d.c.; closes 57 deg. after b.d.c.

Exhaust opens 57 deg. before b.d.c.; closes 15 deg. after t.d.c.

Overlap 30 deg.

The valves have duplex springs, and are operated by short thimble tappets of cast-iron which reciprocate in cast-iron bushes shrunk into the alloy head casting. The clearance of valve to tappet is adjusted by the use of pads of various thicknesses between the valve stem and tappet. These pads are available in thicknesses from .085 in. to .105 in., in steps of .001 in.

The two camshafts, running immediately above the tappets, are made of chill-cast iron, and each is carried in four Vandervell thin-wall steel-backed bearings. They are driven by a Renold duplex roller chain drive in two stages, using chain of .375 in. pitch. The first stage takes the drive from the crankshaft to an intermediate wheel which is keyed to the hub of the second-stage driving wheel, these two wheels running as a unit, and having steel-backed white metal bushes for their bearing on the intermediate spindle.

A chain tensioner of the spring-blade type is provided on the outside of the non-driving strand of the first-stage chain. On the driving side, a fibre block is fitted just clear of the chain, to damp out any undue vibration.

The second stage of the drive is taken from the intermediate driving wheel (looking from the front) around the inlet camshaft wheel, under an idler, and around the exhaust camshaft wheel. The layout is shown in the illustration on page 82. The idler is mounted on an eccentric spindle to allow for adjustment of the chain tension. A serrated plate is fixed to the idler pinion spindle, with two spring-loaded plungers engaging the serrations.

Rotation of the plate, which in turn rotates the eccentric spindle, provides correct chain tension, with one or other of the plungers locking the plate. After adjusting, the idler spindle is firmly tightened by a locknut. The adjusting device is normally enclosed by a breather housing, clearly seen in the illustration of the engine, page 92.

For initial timing of the camshafts, an ingenious arrangement of serrations is used on the camshaft chainwheels and their flanges. The chainwheel assembly is also provided with a threaded boss co-axial with the camshaft when in the normal position. When it is required to remove the cylinder head, the chainwheels and their serrated plates can be removed from the camshafts in a unit by withdrawal of two setscrews, without disturbing the original timing. The threaded bosses above-mentioned run in clearance slots in a fixed bracket bolted to the timing housing. After uncoupling the wheels and slackening the adjusting idler, nuts can be run on to the bosses, and the wheels slid along the slots clear of the camshafts, the chain drive thus being held firmly, out of the way of operations, with no danger of " losing " the timing.

Auxiliary drives

A skew gear at the front end of the crankshaft drives an inclined shaft for the oil-pump and distributor. The latter is by Lucas, with centrifugal and vacuum-operated advance and retard mechanism. 14-mm. spark plugs are mounted vertically in the combustion chambers, to one side of a line drawn through the valve-stem axes.

The oil-pump is of conventional gear-type and draws its supply from the sump, which is made in DTD 424 alloy, through a floating intake with gauze strainer; this fitting ensures that the oil is drawn from near the surface where foreign matter is unlikely to be found. The pump delivers to a full-flow filter of Tecalemit type mounted on the outside of the crankcase, a relief valve being also provided at this point. The oil then enters the main gallery which is situated on the engine offside, transverse drillings leading from the gallery to the main bearing housings. These are provided with annuli, from which four holes convey the lubricant through the bearing shells. The crankshaft is drilled for big-end lubrication, while the small-ends receive a pressure supply as already detailed.

An external pipe is also supplied from the rear main bearing feed, and this leads to the rear camshaft bearings. Longitudinal drillings in the camshafts supply each of the camshaft bearings, while the cams are flooded by overflow from the bearings. The oil returns to the crankcase by way of the front end of the housing, passing over the second-stage drive chain on its way. The first stage chain is lubricated by oil-jet from a drilling taken off the front main bearing supply, while the intermediate and top idler chainwheels are fed by troughs combined with their mountings, in conjunction with suitable oilways. The pump and distributor shaft gears are also provided with an individual oil-jet.

The cooling system

A gallery running on the cylinder block nearside receives water from the pump, the latter being driven by belt from the crankshaft and having the cooling fan mounted on its shaft. From the block, passages convey the water to the head, the direction of flow being designed to eliminate hot-spots. From the head, the flow passes through holes in the offside to the jacketed-induction manifold, from whence it goes finally to the header tank. The system ensures quick warming-up of the jackets, since the jacket water circulation is not influenced by the pump.

The water-jacketed induction manifold has six ports " out," and is of rectangular section. The starting carburetter delivers to a mid-point, where there is also a metered restriction hole aimed at maintaining the necessary balance between the two carburetters. The latter are S.U., of $1\frac{3}{4}$ in. bore. The auxiliary starting carburetter is automatically operated.

CHAPTER 12

Break with the Orthodox—The Jowett

The flat-four—Crankcase assembly—Connecting rods and pistons—
Cylinder heads and valve gear—The lubrication system—Auxiliary drives—
The R4 engine

The flat-four

In view of its complete breakaway from the conventional
in regard to its cylinder layout, it is not surprising to find that
the Jowett flat-four power unit incorporates many constructional features which at once stamp it as a thorough-
bred. The two versions—Javelin and Jupiter—both follow the
same basic design, and in fact the latter engine (used in the
open car) is to all intents and purposes a specially tuned version
of the more normal unit which powers the saloon.

The four cylinders have a bore and stroke of 72.5 by 90
mm., giving a swept volume of 1,485 c.c. The Javelin
produces 52 b.h.p. at 4,100 r.p.m. on a comp. r. of 7.2 : 1,
while the Jupiter develops 62.5 b.h.p. at 4,500 r.p.m. with
7.6 : 1 comp. r. Maximum torque in the latter case, given
at 3,000 r.p.m., is 84 lb. ft., corresponding to a b.m.e.p. of
131 lb. per sq. in.

The engine is illustrated on page 188.

The crankcase assembly

The necessity of having two cylinder blocks disposed one
on either side of the crankcase has not occasioned an excessive
number of joint faces. The construction makes use of a
single light alloy casting for crankcase and cylinder blocks,
split vertically on the centre-line of the crankshaft. Wet
cylinder liners are inserted in the alloy blocks, being a push-fit
therein and having joint rings under the lower flanges. The
liners stand proud of the cylinder heads before the latter are
bolted down, and are thus securely held after final assembly.

The E.N. 12 steel crankshaft runs in three thin-wall bearings located by dowels in the split crankcase-halves. The rear bearing takes the crankshaft end-thrust on flanges, and has a white-metal lining. The other two bearings are copper-lead lined.

The flywheel is mounted on a flange and retained by four setscrews and a dowel. A lipped oil-seal is provided in the clutch housing wall, with its lip towards the crankcase. The shaft is counterbalanced, the main bearing journals having a

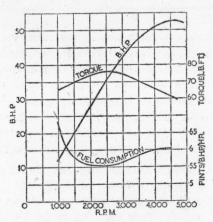

PERFORMANCE GRAPH OF THE JOWETT
" JAVELIN " ENGINE

diameter of 2.25 in. and the big-ends 2 in. On the front end of the shaft are mounted the oil-pump drive skew gear, timing chain pinion, and fan pulley, in that order. A single Woodruff key secures all three items, which are retained by the starting-handle dog screwed into the front of the shaft and locked by a tab washer. The oil-retaining device is formed by the pulley hub running in a lipped seal fitted in the timing cover.

Connecting rods and pistons

The steel connecting rods are split diagonally at the big-ends and have serrated joint faces, the angle of the split being 47 deg. to a line along the rod axis. The big-end bearings are of the thin-wall white-metal lined steel-backed type, the caps being retained by two ⅜ in. diameter bolts. The small-end bush is lead-bronze lined, and lubricated by splash. The split-skirt pistons are aluminium silicon die castings, fitted with two compression and one scraper ring, all above the gudgeon pin. The top ring is chromium plated. The 12/16 in. diameter gudgeon pin is fully floating in both piston bosses and small-end bush, and is retained by circlips. The pistons can be withdrawn from the top, as the big-ends will pass through the cylinder bores.

The cylinder heads and valve gear

Each cylinder head incorporates two combustion chambers, and is an iron casting. The combustion chambers are of bath-tub formation, the valves being slightly inclined and giving a slightly greater depth of chamber where the sparking plugs are located, and a " squish" area opposite these. The four valves (for two cylinders) are arranged in a single row, and are non-interchangeable. Inlet valves are of silicon chrome steel, with head diameter of 1 7/16 in., while the exhaust valves, of Austenitic steel, have a head diameter of 1 7/32 in. The seat angles are respectively 30 and 45 deg., the lift in each case being .315 in. Duplex valve springs are fitted, with split-cone cotter fixing.

The camshaft is driven by a Renold .375-in. pitch duplex roller chain running on 21- and 42-tooth wheels. The short-centre drive has no tensioning arrangement. The camshaft runs in three 1½ in. diameter bearings direct in the crankcase. Its end-float is controlled by a spring-loaded plunger bearing on a bolt-head in the timing-case.

The tappets are of the barrel type, sliding directly in the crankcase, and having a special oil supply from the pressure side of the pump into the tappet holes. The tubular push-rods are 5/16 in. diameter, and their adjustment is at the top, on the rocker in the normal manner.

The rockers are bushed, and carried on a tubular shaft supported by two pillars. They are located by spacing springs which also aid noise reduction. The valve timing is as follows :—

Inlet opens 12 deg. before t.d.c.; closes 53 deg. after b.d.c.

Exhaust opens 50 deg. before b.d.c.; closes 15 deg. after t.d.c.

Overlap 27 deg.

Each cylinder head has a siamesed inlet port feeding the two valves, and two separate exhaust ports. The inlet ports on each head are connected by a balance pipe, a separate carburetter being, of course, fitted to each port, in a position giving an admirable " drop-in " feed. The carburetters are Zenith type 30 VIG5.

The lubrication system

An oil-pump of the usual gear type is driven from the crankshaft at half engine speed by skew gearing. An extension from the pump shaft also drives the ignition distributor.

The pump draws oil through a gauze strainer at the bottom of the 9-pint sump, via a large-diameter suction pipe. The pump delivery passes to oilways which lead to a full-flow filter of Vokes type mounted externally. The Jupiter engine has, in addition, an oil-cooler of 1 pint capacity bracket-mounted to the engine front and connected by external flexible piping in series with the filter and oil galleries.

The pressure supply from the filter (or cooler) passes to galleries formed in each crankcase half, and lubricating the tappets, main bearings and camshaft bearings by suitable oil-ways. The overhead rocker gear is fed by leads from each gallery incorporated in the cylinder head studs. The crank-shaft is drilled for big-end lubrication in the normal manner.

Pressure relief in case of the filter element becoming choked is provided by spring-loading the element itself inside its housing. The pump by-pass relief valve is contained in the pump cover, and is non-adjustable, being set at about 70 lb. per sq. in.

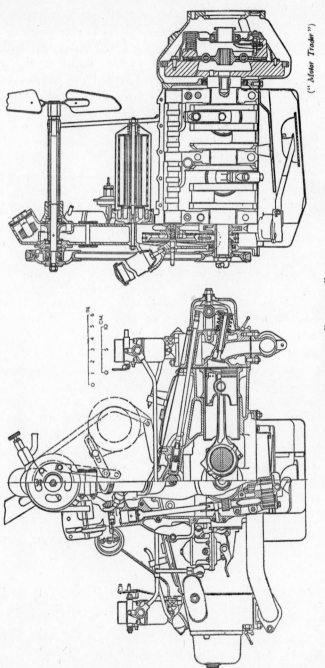

("*Motor Trader*")

SECTION OF THE JOWETT "JAVELIN" ENGINE

Auxiliary drives

The Lucas distributor, type DKYH4A, driven from an extension of the oil-pump drive in an approximately vertical plane, is accessibly mounted high on the engine front. The centrifugally operated advance and retard mechanism commences at the low speed of 600 r.p.m. The standard plugs are Champion L10s, with a gap of .020 to .025 in.

The centrifugal type water pump is driven by vee-belt from the crankshaft at engine speed, and delivers 7.5 gals. per min. at 2,100 r.p.m. It has a rubber and carbon seal on each side of the impeller. A long rearward extension of the pump shaft, carried in widely-spaced bearings, drives the fan for the radiator which in this vehicle is mounted behind the power unit.

A non-adjustable thermostat is fitted in the delivery hose between the pump and radiator header tank.

A sectional drawing of the engine is on page 149.

The R4 engine

Announced in October, 1953, the type R4 Jupiter competition-type car is powered by the normal design of engine, but with a compression ratio of 8.5 : 1, developing 64 h.p. at 4,300 r.p.m., and capable of running up to well over 5,000 r.p.m. A feature of more than usual interest on this engine is the incorporation of a cooling fan, driven independently of the engine by a battery operated electric motor. The motor is switched on thermostatically whenever the coolant temperature calls for the fan to augment the natural air-flow through the radiator, i.e., in traffic or when hill-climbing under certain conditions. In normal running, of course, the fan will not be required, so that there is no unwanted power loss from this source.

CHAPTER 13

A Big Four—The Lea-Francis

*A long-stroke unit—The valve gear—The main casting—Connecting rods and pistons—
Auxiliary drives—The lubrication system*

A long-stroke unit

There are several features of the Lea-Francis engine which stamp it as unusual, if not unique. Firstly, it is one of the few power units of well over 2 litres having only four cylinders and a considerable length of stroke. Then its valve-gear arrangement achieves the desirable hemispherical combustion chamber shape with simplicity in the operating mechanism, but also coupled with lightness of valve-gear reciprocating parts almost on a par with the best overhead-camshaft layouts.

With a bore and stroke of 85 by 110 mm., giving a swept volume of 2,496 c.c., the Lea-Francis engine develops 100 b.h.p. at 4,000 r.p.m., on a comp. r. of 7 : 1. Maximum b.m.e.p., obtained at 2,500 r.p.m., is 140 lb. per sq. in., corresponding to a torque of 142 lb. ft. Various compression ratios can be obtained by the use of specially crowned pistons, and with a comp. r. of 7.63 : 1, plus camshafts designed to give a higher lift than standard, 120 to 125 b.h.p. can be obtained at 5,200 r.p.m. These revolutions may appear high when considering the relatively long stroke of 110 mm., but the piston speed is still well under 4,000 ft. per min., which is not unduly rapid when allied to components of the high grade pattern associated with this type of engine.

The valve gear

The hemispherical combustion chambers of the four cylinders each carry inclined valves at an included angle of 80 deg. Separate camshafts operate the inlet and exhaust valves, the shafts being positioned high up, one on each side of the cylinder block just below the head joint. The head itself is thus clear of operating mechanism other than the rockers, allowing the spark plugs to be accessibly positioned vertically in the combustion chambers between the valve ports. (See illustrations, page 95.) Due, however, to the camshaft location, the push-rods are extremely short and light, and with the consequent reduction in inertia, the rockers themselves can be lightened considerably. Further, valve-rocker clearance can be expected to remain more constant with the change of temperature, since the dimensional variation with heat will be small.

The rockers are housed in pairs in four separate boxes,

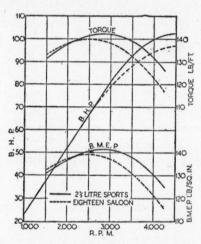

PERFORMANCE GRAPH OF THE 2½-LITRE
LEA-FRANCIS ENGINE

each box carrying its own rocker-shaft and having a detachable lid for inspection and adjustment. The camshaft housings are cast in the cylinder block casting, and are provided with transverse webs forming four of the camshaft bearings, a fifth bearing (per shaft) being located in the front wall of the casting.

The two camshafts are of Monikrom alloy cast iron, and are driven by a Renold .375 in. pitch duplex roller chain. Each of the camshaft chainwheels, of 44 teeth, is secured to its camshaft hub by four bolts and nuts, the holes being slotted to allow some rotational adjustment margin. The method of obtaining this adjustment is interesting, and consists of two dowels connecting the chainwheel and flange, located on the same " circle " as the four bolts and nuts and diametrically opposite to one another. They are held to the chainwheel by nuts and washers, and are screwdriver-slotted at this end also. The other end, of each dowel, locating in a slot in the camshaft flange, is eccentric to the main axis of the dowel. Thus, slackening of the nut, and rotation of the dowel by a screwdriver in the slotted end, will move the chainwheel radially in relation to the camshaft. The actual range of movement is 10 deg., which is much in excess of that provided by moving the wheel through one chain pitch. Consequently, there is, in effect, limitless adjustment.

Once the dowels have been set, and their nuts tightened, the chainwheels can, if required, be removed from the camshafts without the setting being lost.

The chain is provided with an eccentrically mounted jockey-wheel on the offside, adjustment of this to effect correct chain tension being feasible without removing the timing cover. Just clear of the nearside run of the chain is a damper block of Tufnol, which controls any undue tendency towards chain whip.

The camshaft drive is shown on page 96.

The tappets are of chilled cast-iron, and take their bearing in the cylinder head casting at an angle of 15 deg. from the vertical. They have steel cups pressed in their upper ends to receive the push-rods. The latter are only 2 9/16 in. long, and are steel stampings with their ball and cup lower and upper ends respectively machined integrally.

The valve head diameters are 1.75 in. and 1.59 in. for inlet and exhaust respectively, the lift being .378 in. in each case. The cast-iron valve guides are interchangeable. Two springs per valve are used, these also being interchangeable between inlets and exhausts. The valve timing is as follows:—

Inlet opens 15 deg. before t.d.c.; closes 55 deg. after b.d.c.

Exhaust opens 55 deg. before b.d.c.; closes 15 deg. after t.d.c.

Overlap 30 deg.

Due to the valve-gear layout, the ports are of considerable length, and generously water-jacketed. The exhaust ports discharge into two manifolds of Y-shape, one serving cylinders 1–2 and the other 3–4. The inlet ports are connected by a water-jacketed manifold provided with two S.U. carburetters.

The 14-mm. spark plugs are positioned vertically in the combustion chambers about $\frac{3}{4}$ in. to the rear of a line drawn through the axes of the two valves.

The main casting

The integral crankcase and cylinder block is an iron casting. It contains, as already mentioned, the camshaft housings at the top, and has a machined face at the front to mate up with the cast aluminium timing housing which is secured thereto by a large number of $\frac{1}{4}$-in. bolts, and encloses the chain drive and tensioner.

The cylinder bores are integral with the main casting, without liners, and have very generous water spaces, there being $\frac{1}{4}$ in. between pairs of cylinders 1–2 and 3–4, and $1\frac{3}{8}$ in. at the centre. The bores are hone-finished. There are three massive webs to carry the main crankshaft bearings, the cast-iron bearing caps of which are recessed into the webs to give positive location. The cap studs are 9/16 in. diameter.

The aluminium flywheel housing is bolted to a machined face at the rear of the crankcase casting, and is positively dowelled for accuracy in positioning relative to the oil-return thread on the crankshaft.

The nickel-iron cast crankshaft is carried on three Glacier bearings comprising white-metal on steel backings, the latter having a thickness of .065 in. The journal diameter is $2\frac{1}{2}$ in., while the length of shaft between the rear of the front bearing and the front of the rear one is only $16\frac{1}{2}$ in., which is indicative of an extremely rigid shaft. The crankpins are $2\frac{3}{8}$ in. diameter. The shaft is located by the rearmost bearing, the front and rear ends of which have flanges for this purpose. At the rear of the back bearing, beyond the oil-thrower, the shaft diameter is increased for the oil-return thread machined thereon. This, as already stated, runs in a register in the fly-wheel housing, and no other sealing arrangement is found necessary, thanks to the large diameter of the thread and the accuracy of fitting.

The steel flywheel is spigot-mounted on the shaft and secured by six bolts.   The starter ring is shrunk-on, on present engines, but was formerly machined on the wheel.

Connecting rods and pistons

The connecting rods are of conventional H-section, of alloy steel, with big-end bearings comprising white-metal, run direct in the rod eyes.   The big-ends are split in the normal manner at right-angles to the rod axis, the caps being held by two bolts separate from the rod material, with their heads registering against the rod shoulders to prevent turning when the nuts are tightened.   The bolts are 7/16 in. diameter, and their dead fit in the cap holes locates the latter with the desired accuracy.

The small-end bushes are bronze, with a drilling, to assist splash lubrication, carried from the top end of the rod.   The bushes are a press fit, and take $\frac{7}{8}$-in. diameter gudgeon pins, which are circlip-located in the piston bosses, and are fully floating.

The aluminium alloy pistons are of Automotive Engineering or Wellworthy make, with two compression and one scraper ring located above the gudgeon pin.   In some types a further oil-control ring is fitted near the bottom of the skirt.   Various heights of piston crown are available for alteration to compression ratio.

The camshaft chain-pinion and fan pulley are located on suitably machined diameters of the crankshaft and fitted on Woodruff keys, being held axially by an end-nut which also carries the starting-handle register.   An oil-seal is housed in the front cover and locates against the rear of the pulley boss. The fan is mounted on ball-bearings inside its forwardly extended pulley boss, the " dead " fan spindle being of alloy steel, screwed into the front of the crankcase casting.   It is further supported by a boss in the timing cover through which it passes.   An ingenious item in this assembly is that by suitable drillings the fan bearings are positively lubricated from the timing cover.

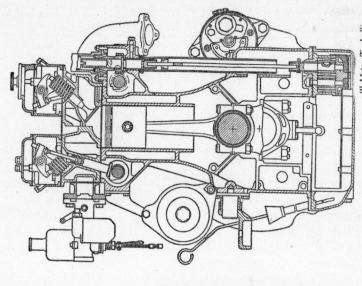

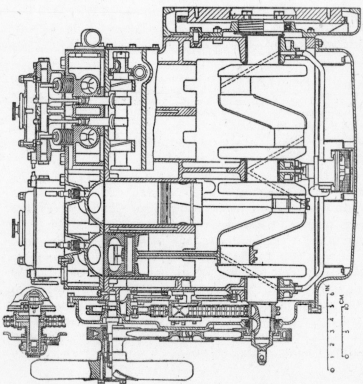

("*Motor Trader*")

SECTION OF THE 2.5-LITRE LEA-FRANCIS ENGINE

Auxiliary drives

The drives for oil-pump, distributor, and water pump are taken from the exhaust camshaft. The two first-named items are driven by spiral gears, the driving gear being about half-way along the camshaft, and engaging the driven gear on a vertical spindle. At the top of this spindle the ignition distributor is located in a very accessible position. The lower extension is, of course, external to the main engine casting, and is carried in a tube down to approximately crankshaft level. From thence the shaft continues, to couple up with the oil-pump housed in the base of the sump.

The water pump is driven by another pair of spiral gears from the camshaft rear end, which has a short extension on which the driving gear is keyed and retained by a nut. The pump spindle is thus at right-angles to the engine centre-line, and runs at 1.9 times camshaft speed.

The water circulation under pump pressure takes place through the cylinder head only. The pump draws from the radiator base and delivers to an inlet elbow at the rear of the cylinder head. The outlet is at the front of the head, via the thermostat, to the radiator header tank, the thermostat by-pass delivering water through the induction manifold jacket and back to the pump intake. The cylinder jackets are cooled by natural circulation through ducts between jackets and head, a feature which is well known as providing rapid warming-up of the jackets and consequent early reduction of piston oil-drag.

The lubrication system

An interesting feature of the lubrication system is the wide use of pipes instead of drilled oil-ducts. The pump is of the conventional gear type, partially submerged in the aluminium alloy sump, and draws through a short pipe from a strainer located on the sump floor at the centre. The pump delivers to a Tecalemit full-flow filter through a duct in the crankcase wall, the filter being fitted externally. From the filter, another duct passes back to the inside of the crank-case, thence to a three-way distributor under the centre bearing of the crankshaft. From this distributor pipes take off to each main bearing. The crankshaft is drilled for big-end lubrication in the usual way.

From the front main bearing, lubricant is taken to a union on the front crankcase wall. From this point a metering jet feeds a drip on to the timing chain pinion teeth, and two pipes take oil up to the camshafts, the bearings of which are fed by drillings. The camshaft housings are kept full of oil to a depth within about $\frac{1}{4}$ in. of the camshaft axes. Thus, the working faces of the cams are lubricated with extreme thoroughness. The overflow drains back into the sump via ducts at the front.

The rocker spindles, and distributor and oil-pump drive spindle, all receive a pressure oil supply by small-bore pipes and ducts. The rockers themselves are drilled to feed oil to the top ends of the push-rods. The rocker-boxes are interconnected by drain passages which in turn drain into the camshaft housings and lubricant also drains down over the push-rods and tappets, ensuring adequate attention at these points.

The engine is illustrated in section on page 156.

CHAPTER 14

Power Without Frills—The M.G.

A simple o.h.v. design—The main assembly—Connecting rods and pistons—
The cylinder head and valve gear—The lubrication system—Auxiliary drives
—The type TF engine

A simple o.h.v. design

The 1950–53 version of the 1,250 c.c. M.G. engine—the TD—differs in only minor respects from its predecessor, the TC. It is an excellent example of what can be achieved from a power unit of relative simple design, by a process of steady development, in conjunction with hard usage in the hands of a large number of enthusiastic drivers.

The M.G. engine makes no recourse to such details as hemispherical combustion heads or twin overhead camshafts, but incorporates a form of combustion chamber which has shown itself peculiarly adept at obtaining high b.m.e.p. figures from relatively low grades of fuel whilst at the same time responding excellently to the use of high-octane and other " premium " brands. (See sectional drawing, page 160.)

The four cylinders measure 66.5 by 90 mm., giving a total swept volume of 1,250 c.c. The normal output is 54.4 b.h.p. at 5,200–5,500 r.p.m., on a comp. r. of 7.25 : 1. The b.m.e.p. (at its maximum at 2,600 r.p.m.) is 125 lb. per sq. in., the corresponding torque figure being 765 lb. in.

The main assembly

A single iron casting forms the cylinder block and crank-case down to the main bearing centre-line. The three main bearings are carried on substantial cross-bearers, and comprise steel white-metal lined split bearing shells which are dowelled in the main casting and bearing caps respectively. Each bearing cap is held by two bolts retained by split-pins. An oil gallery cast along the crankcase nearside supplies the bearings via transverse drillings to each top shell. The crank-

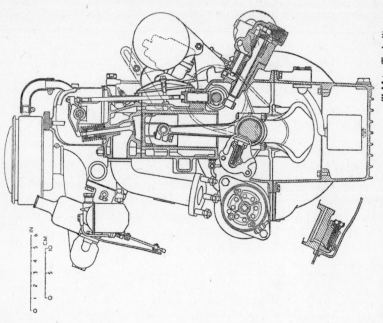

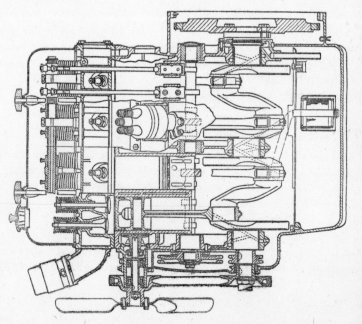

("Motor Trader")

shaft end-float is controlled by the centre bearing which has faced flanges on either side allowing about .0015 in. total float.

The steel crankshaft is fully counterbalanced, and has main journals with a diameter of 52 mm., the big-ends being 45 mm. At the rear of the shaft is an attachment flange for the flywheel, which is secured thereto by four setscrews and two dowels.

Between the rear main bearing and the flywheel flange is an oil return thread, operating in a split collector housing, the two halves of which are formed in the crankcase casting

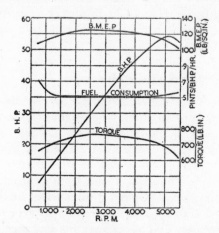

PERFORMANCE GRAPH OF THE M.G. MIDGET
TD ENGINE

and sump respectively. A drain pipe leads from this housing, down into the bottom of the sump.

At the front, the shaft carries the timing chain pinion and the fan pulley which are secured by separate Woodruff keys and have an oil thrower sandwiched between them. The items are retained by the starting handle dog which screws into the shaft, and is shimmed as required to give the correct positioning of the handle relative to the compression pressure.

The oil sealing arrangements at the timing drive end comprise a split oil seal of composite material, one half of which is held in a groove formed in the timing chain cover, and the other half in a corresponding recess in the sump casting.

L

Connecting rods and pistons

The steel connecting rods have steel-backed thin-wall big-end bearings with white metal linings, the bearing halves being tab-located. Fitted bolts locate the caps. The small-end eyes of the rods are split, and provided with a pinch-bolt which rigidly clamps the gudgeon pin therein. The pin has a circumferential groove engaging the pinch-bolt and preventing endwise movement.

The aluminium alloy pistons are of Aerolite make, having oval skirts, and two compression and one scraper ring located above the gudgeon pin. The latter, of course, oscillate in the piston bosses only, being clamped rigidly in the connecting rod small-ends.

The cylinder head and valve gear

The single camshaft is mounted on the nearside of the crankcase, and runs in three white-metal bushes. The front bush is a press fit in the crankcase wall, while the centre one is split, and located by a setscrew. The rear bush is also set-screw located. Camshaft end-float is controlled by a thrust plate between the chainwheel and front bearing. The cam-shaft drive comprises a Renold duplex roller chain of .375 in. pitch, provided with a spring-loaded slipper type tensioner, the contacting surfaces of which engage the chain rollers, and not the side-plates. A pressure oil supply is fed to the tensioner barrel via a metering hole, giving a degree of hydraulic damping to prevent undue oscillation of the slipper. The oil escapes from the barrel through a hole which feeds it on to the chain rollers.

The camshaft operates barrel-type tappets working directly in the crankcase, and recessed at the top to take the steel push-rods.

The iron cylinder head is held by ten studs and nuts spaced evenly around the casting. The combustion chambers are of " bath-tub " formation, with a slightly greater depth at the nearside, which is where the sparking plugs are fitted. This shape is achieved by slightly inclining the overhead valves towards the offside, where a " squish " area is formed by the junction of the head casting with the block. The valves are arranged in a single row, and are not interchangeable, the head diameter being 33 mm. for inlet and 31 mm. for exhaust valves. The valve lift in each case is .375 in., and the face angle 30 deg.

Duplex valve springs are retained by cups with split-cone cotter fixing. Particular care is taken to ensure freedom from oil passing down the valve stems. Shrouds are fitted between each inner spring and valve guide and on each valve stem is a synthetic rubber sealing ring located just below the split-cone fixing. In this manner, oiling-up troubles are obviated, while at the same time ample clearance can be allowed between valve stems and guides to ensure correct valve action at high engine speeds. The rocker gear comprises a single rocker-shaft carried on four pillars bolted to the head. The shaft is located by key-washers engaging slots in the centre pair of pillars, this preventing rotation of the shaft. The shaft holes in the pillars are split to one side of the pillars, and are thus pinched firmly to the shaft when the pillars are bolted down. The rockers are bushed, and positioned by spacing springs which also minimize rocker noise. The valve timing is as follows :—

Inlet opens 11 deg. before t.d.c.; closes 57 deg. after b.d.c.

Exhaust opens 52 deg. before b.d.c.; closes 24 deg. after t.d.c.

Overlap 35 deg.

The four exhaust ports are separate, and deliver into a four-branch manifold having a junction for the branches some way from the ports and feeding into a single pipe. The inlet ports are siamesed as between cylinders 1–2 and 3–4. An unjacketed cast-iron induction manifold feeds the two inlet ports from two S.U. carburetters, a large-diameter balance pipe connecting the two tracts.

The lubrication system

A gear oil-pump of conventional type is spigot-mounted high up on the nearside of the crankcase, and driven from the camshaft by skew gears. It draws from the aluminium oil-sump via an internal pipe of large diameter which connects with a suction strainer of gauze mounted slightly to the rear in the sump. The pressure delivery goes to a full-flow filter of Wilmot-Breeden, Tecalemit, or Puralator type, and from thence to the main oil gallery. Relief valves are provided for pump by-pass and also for filter stoppage.

The main oil gallery supplies the main bearings in the manner already described. The crankshaft is drilled in the usual way for big-end lubrication. The big-ends themselves are further drilled through to the outside of the rod eye, the direction of the drilling being such that a spray of oil is directed on to the cylinder wall on the thrust side. From the

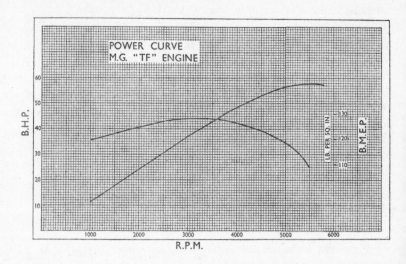

rear of the oil gallery, an external pipe leads up to the cylinder head, from whence a drilling conveys oil to the rear rocker-shaft pillar, and thus to the hollow rocker-shaft. From here, oilways lead to the rocker bushes, and along each rocker to an outlet hole which supplies the top cup-ends of the push-rods and the thrust ends of the valve-stems. The oil returns to the crankcase by way of the push-rod housing.

From the front camshaft bearing, the escaping oil is fed into an annulus in the chainwheel, from which holes lead on to the teeth. A shroud plate ensures that the lubricant follows the correct path. In addition, the chain receives extra oil from the tensioner, as already mentioned.

Auxiliary drives

The ignition distributor is located on the same side of the engine as the oil-pump, to the rear of it, and driven by a separate pair of skew gears. These two pairs of gears are actually located one on each side of the camshaft centre bearing. The distributor is spigot-mounted, and has centrifugally operated automatic advance mechanism. The sparking plugs are 14 mm. size, Champion make being standard.

The water-pump body is formed as part of the main casting, just below the head joint. It delivers the water into the jackets, from where the flow is through passages into the head, the direction being aimed at eliminating hot spots. The take-off to the radiator header tank is from an elbow at the front of the head, a thermostat being fitted at this point.

The fan is mounted on the pump spindle, the overhanging extension being carried on two ball-bearings. A spring-loaded carbon and rubber sealing arrangement prevents water leakage along the pump shaft, but provision is made for the escape of any water before it reaches the fan bearings. A single vee-belt transmits the drive from the crankshaft to the fan and water-pump.

The carburetters are of the S.U. semi-downdraught type, $1\frac{1}{4}$-in. bore, with hand mixture control for starting.

The type TF engine

Introduced in October, 1953, the type TF engine is similar in general design to the TD unit, but in view of the general availability of premium grades of fuel, modifications have been made enabling greater power to be produced. The maximum b.h.p. is 57.5 at 5,500 r.p.m.

The TF engine incorporates many of the features which formerly came under the heading of Stage 2 tuning, as detailed in Chapter 22. Larger valves are fitted than on the standard TD, the head diameters being 36 and 34 mm. for inlet and exhaust respectively. 150-lb. valve springs are also a standard fitting, and $1\frac{1}{2}$-in. carburetters are used.

The rocker clearances are .012 in. hot, the valve timing being as follows:—

Inlet valve opens 5 deg. before t.d.c.; closes 45 deg. after b.d.c.

Exhaust valve opens 45 deg. before b.d.c.; closes 5 deg. after t.d.c.

Overlap 10 deg.

It will be noted that the overlap period is considerably less than that on the TD engine, the object being evidently the maintenance of good torque at lower r.p.m., in spite of the lower gas speeds at this point due to the use of larger inlet valves. The comp. r. is 8 : 1. Performance curves are shown on page 164.

PART 2

TUNING AND MODIFYING FOR PERFORMANCE

Introduction		... ...	168
Chapter	15.	The Cylinder Head	170
,,	16.	Modifications to Valve Gear	198
,,	17.	Attention to Cylinders and Pistons ...	205
,,	18.	Choice of Compression Ratio	213
,,	19.	Tuning the Ford Ten	219
,,	20.	Tuning the Jaguar	232
,,	21.	Tuning the Jowett	238
,,	22.	Tuning the M.G.	247
,,	23.	Miscellaneous Engine Tuning	257
,,	24.	Rational Supercharging	262
,,	25.	Appendices	272

Introduction to Part 2

When considering modifications to existing power units with the object of obtaining increased performance, the first consideration should be—what is this performance to be used for?

There is little doubt that the needs of the majority of road-users can be met by the power available from a standard engine, always providing it is operating at maximum efficiency; in other words, that it is maintained in correct condition. It is probably true to say that this condition does not obtain on 75 per cent. of modern cars on the road to-day, and that such are running below par due to lack of maintenance, maladjustment, use of unsuitable fuel and lubricants, and so on. It cannot be emphasized too strongly that tuning methods involving modifications to components should never be resorted to in an endeavour to rectify power loss caused by errors and omissions such as the above.

However, there are always the drivers whose appreciation of a good car and aptitude in driving enable them to make use of more power than is obtainable from the standard engine, even in normal road usage. Competition drivers come in another category, there being very few types of event in which an engine rather more powerful than standard is not a decided advantage. On the other hand, power costs money. The type of engine with which we are concerned is tolerably efficient in the way it burns its fuel, and thus any increase in output from the crankshaft demands the burning of more heat energy. Also, some extra maintenance costs must be accepted, as increase in heat flow, plus the higher r.p.m. (which is certain to be maintained, if only for the sheer pleasure of doing so), leaves its marks on such items as valve faces, spark plugs, and so on.

It will be evident from a study of Part 1 of the book that too much emphasis should not be placed on sheer b.h.p. at high revolutions, when considering power increases. A useful addition to the torque over a wide speed range may well prove more suitable for some forms of motoring than a lot of extra power at top revolutions. These things can only be decided in the light of the use to which the car will be put.

An important item, in the case of engines whose makers operate an engine-exchange scheme, is that no unit will be accepted for exchange if it has been rendered non-standard. It is necessary to bear this in mind when increases in port or valve sizes, or machining for compression ratio increase, are in mind. In the case of o.h.v. engines, of course, a spare head gets over most if not all of the difficulty.

CHAPTER 15

The Cylinder Head

Some general points—Improving volumetric efficiency—The inlet tract—
Oversize valves—Attention to the exhaust side—Valves, springs and collars—
Exhaust pipe layout

Some general points

In view of the number of books available dealing with the inspection, measurement for wear, and overhaul of power units, it is not proposed to go into much detail in regard to what might be termed the more straightforward items, it being assumed that the owner of a competition-type engine who is considering the various implications of looking for more power, will be conversant with the normal methods of checking for wear and fitness for the job of the various components. However, a brief reference to one or two of the most important points to be watched will not be amiss, while information on specific items aiming at higher efficiency will be given in detail.

It will be obvious that any examination of the engine, prior to undertaking modification, must be ruthless, particularly if it has seen a good deal of service. It is not very helpful to suggest that components showing undue signs of wear should be replaced, since what might be allowable in ordinary motoring might spell trouble at high speed and load. The aim should always be to have all clearances correct.

The most important items in the whole engine are, of course, the cylinders and pistons. Careful measurement will show their condition as regards wear, while examination with the aid of a small inspection lamp inside each bore will show up any discoloration, scratches or scores, the cause of which must naturally be tracked down. The more particular requirements for high-speed operation are considered in a later chapter.

Gudgeon pins usually have a clearance in the piston bosses of about .0015 in. per in. of pin diameter, but this will vary for special types of piston.

Fully floating pins with end-pads should have from .003 to .004 in. end-play, while pins retained by circlips should abut hard against the circlip at each end.   Connecting rod big-end bearing clearances vary a good deal, depending on the material, bearing area, and oil-feed characteristics, and the same remark applies to main bearings.   Data relating to these must be obtained, if required, from the manufacturers, and it is unwise to rely on the opinion of well-meaning " experts."

Camshaft bearings usually wear very slowly, as the shaft speed and bearing loading is relatively low.   The normal type of white-metal bushed sleeve bearing has a clearance of about .002 in. per in. of diameter.   Ball and roller bearings require special consideration.

Auxiliary drives, whether by chain or gears, do not present any trouble, as replacement of components is not difficult. Valve gear usually calls for special consideration, since many commercial assemblies lack the precision of fitting which is essential for high-speed operation.

Improving volumetric efficiency

Irrespective of the type of fuel used, or compression ratio employed, the highest possible breathing efficiency must be aimed at.   We have seen from a study of Part I how the designer tackles this particular aspect.   In its passage through the factory, however, the product as made is liable to become subject to minor imperfections in machining and so on, which must be corrected if the original intentions are to be achieved, and are an essential preliminary to subsequent operations. The cylinder head and valve gear will provide a useful start to these operations.

It is highly probable that an engine of the o.h.v. type will be dealt with, but obviously, any engine, even of originally sober design with side-valves, will benefit by having the induction ports and passages as free from obstruction as possible.   Whilst the emphasis is on the inlet side, a free exhaust is, of course, highly desirable, if only from the point of view of ensuring a reasonable running temperature.   An incidental improvement in power output is likely to be obtained, in addition, by virtue of exhaust extractor action, in a well-designed system.

The typical o.h.v. engine will have the valves arranged either in a parallel row more or less centrally in the head, or in two rows at an angle to each other. Most of the modifications apply with equal force to either layout, but there are one or two items which lend themselves particularly to the hemispherical-head inclined-valve arrangement, and these will be specially mentioned.

In the design of the inlet tract, there are three factors to be considered, namely, valve size, port and manifold shape, and carburetter bore size. These three factors are closely inter-related, and any modifications must therefore be designed with regard to the effect on the whole combination. For example, the fitting of large-bore carburetters without any other modifications would have no advantage (unless the original instruments were far too small); in fact the performance would in all probability be impaired, because of the reduced gas speed. Increasing valve and port sizes, while of benefit at very high speeds, would again be liable to affect the low-speed torque. Larger carburetters, plus an increase in valve and inlet tract size, undoubtedly show an appreciable b.h.p. increase through about the last one-third of the power curve, and this is a modification of interest to those concerned with sports-car racing.

For those who desire a performance rather better than standard for normal road use, an inexpensive modification can be carried out to the existing valves which is well worth while, as it does not impair the low-speed pulling power but gives a little more pep at high revs. The existing valve seats will probably be found to have a gas-seal with the valve, of about 3/32 in. wide. However, a perfectly adequate seal can be obtained with a seat having a width as small as 1/16 in., or even 1/32 in. The object aimed at is best explained by the diagrams on page 173. The first one shows the valve and seat as standard, the dotted lines indicating the proposed narrow seat. Reference to the lower diagram shows how, with this revised seat width, the outside diameter of the valve head can be reduced from A to B, while at the same time the port size is increased from X to Y. It will be obvious that the increased diameter of port, and reduction in valve diameter, will give a slightly easier gas flow at high engine r.p.m.

The work involved is not difficult to carry out, but must be carefully done. The reduction in valve diameter can be done by mounting the valve stem in a drill chuck, or better still, a lathe, and removing the surplus metal with a file, finishing off with emery cloth. The outer diameter should be nicely radiused off, but the valve should not be reduced in

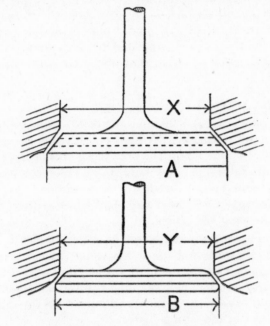

MODIFICATION TO STANDARD INLET VALVE
AND PORTS TO GIVE EASIER GAS FLOW

thickness, the radius being used to merge the narrowed seat into the valve body.

As regards enlarging the port, a cutter is the ideal method, but if this cannot be managed, files and scrapers provide a satisfactory substitute. Care is necessary to ensure that there is plenty of room past the valve all round its circumference, when in the open position. There should be at least 1 mm. between the valve edge and the nearest combustion-chamber wall.

The protruding inlet valve guide forms what might be called a major obstruction, and some enthusiasts make a habit of cutting off the guide flush with the inside of the port. If this leaves a reasonable length or guide *in situ*, there is probably no harm done. At least equal, and usually better, results will be obtained if the protruding part of the guide in the port is streamlined in the direction of gas flow so as to present a knife-edge on the approach and exit sides. At its narrowest part (at right-angles to the gas stream) the guide thickness should be such as to leave about 1/16 in. of metal between the hole in the guide and its outside wall. The obstruction to gas flow presented by a streamlined guide of this type is much less than that of the circular valve stem.

The inlet tract

The inlet ports and the inlet manifold should have a dead-smooth finish internally. A high polish is not necessary, but sets the seal on the job. The port shape should not be altered unless the valve openings have been enlarged, and in the latter case the endeavour should be to obtain a gradual and consistent decrease in bore size right through from the valve seat to the manifold flange.

Cleaning-up ports and manifold in this manner is a tedious job, and the work is made much easier if small rotary files and polishers can be used, in conjunction with one of the high-speed portable motors now readily obtainable. Care must be taken in using such equipment not to remove too much metal in the wrong place.

The manifold flanges form a frequent source of obstruction to smooth gas flow, as it is comparatively rare for these either to meet perfectly or to be of identical size of mating aperture. Any error can be seen by clamping a sheet of white cartridge paper between the flanges and bolting-up, the flanges having previously been lightly smeared with graphite. Having noted on removal of the paper the dimensional differences between the flanges reproduced on either side of the paper, correction is carried out by filing or the use of the mechanical equipment mentioned above. The same procedure can be carried out on the flanges between the manifold and the carburetters.

The foregoing attention to standard fittings will unquestion-ably result in considerable improvement to the induction side which will show throughout the power range. However, it may be desired to increase peak performance, even at the expense of power lower down, and for this purpose larger size inlet valves can be usefully employed. It should be borne in mind that this is a fairly far-reaching modification, and the characteristics of the power flow, in regard to normal road usage, may not be so pleasant as on the unaltered engine.

Oversize valves

Some makers actually market oversized valves, there being sufficient metal in the head casting to allow of these being fitted into suitably enlarged ports. Instructions for fitting are provided for the asking, but as the amount of metal to be removed is appreciable, the only practical way of doing the job is by means of a side-and-face cutter of correct size, using the valve-guide as a pilot hole.

When modifying an engine in this manner without, as it were, the makers' blessing, the amount of metal between the valve seats is usually the factor controlling the size. The main

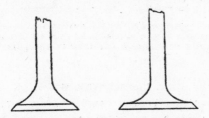

THE TULIP-SHAPED INLET VALVE SHOWN ON LEFT GIVES A MORE EFFECTIVE GAS FLOW THAN THE NORMAL FLAT-SHAPED VALVE ON RIGHT

point is not to be too ambitious, as a millimetre or two on valve diameter means quite a lot in terms of opening area. Also, the exhaust valve can quite well be left alone, and the enlargement confined to the inlet, with little disadvantage.

When the engine makers are unwilling or unable to supply oversize valves, these can be obtained from specialist manu-facturers, or in some cases it may be found that valves from a larger engine can be adapted. It is, however, necessary to ensure that the material is adequate for the job, and also it is worth while taking some care in choosing the shape. The " tulip " shape shown on page 175 is more effective in directing the gas flow into the port than the flat shape which is still employed occasionally.

As regards the ports required for larger valves, attention to these does not differ materially from the operations already described when modifying standard valves. There is the important point, however, that it is sometimes possible to obtain a better shape of port, particularly on older engines having inclined valves. Some of these used a somewhat wide angle between the valves, possibly with the object of obtaining some cooling influence on the exhaust valve, from the incoming

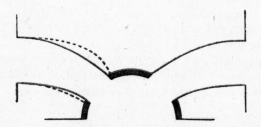

ENLARGEMENT OF INLET PORTS TO TAKE LARGER VALVES ON HEMISPHERI-
CALLY HEADED ENGINES CAN SOMETIMES BE MADE TO GIVE A BETTER GAS
FLOW INTO THE CYLINDER, AS SHOWN BY THE DOTTED LINES

inlet flow. The same characteristic was liable to cause inter-port gas leakage to a greater extent than if the inlet flow was directed more into the cylinder bore. The latter effect can be obtained, where there is sufficient metal, by altering the port shape as shown.

Attention to the exhaust side

The problems associated with the exhaust valves and ports are quite different from those applicable to the inlet side, as will be evident from a study of Chapter 2. The residue of the heat produced has to be ejected via the exhaust valves and ports, and for this reason care must be taken in

(*Continued on page* 193)

TWO CARBURETTERS ARE ACCOMMODATED ON MR. V. A. FOX'S MANIFOLD
CONVERSION FOR THE FORD "CONSUL" ENGINE

MR. V. A. FOX'S MANIFOLD CONVERSION ON THE FORD "CONSUL" ENGINE

M

MR. V. A. FOX'S CON-
VERSION ON THE FORD
" CONSUL " ENGINE

EXHIBITION MODEL OF FORD 10 ENGINE FITTED UP WITH AQUAPLANE EQUIPMENT.
THE CYLINDER HEAD IS RAISED AND " MIRRORED " TO SHOW THE COMBUSTION
CHAMBERS

178

THE DAVIES SPECIAL INTAKE AND EXHAUST MANIFOLD FOR THE FORD 1,172-C.C.
ENGINE. TWIN S.U. CARBURETTERS ARE USED

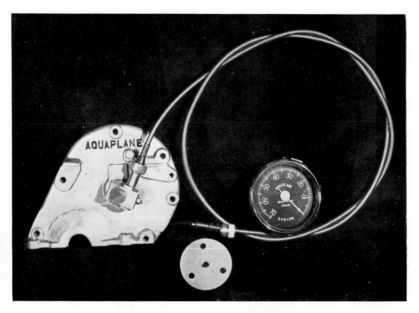

AQUAPLANE ALLOY TIMING CASE COVER WITH TACHOMETER AND DRIVE, FOR FORD 10

AQUAPLANE ALLOY RACING FLYWHEEL FOR FORD 10. AQUAPLANE
EXHAUST MANIFOLD FOR FORD 10

(*Left*) AQUAPLANE ALLOY CYLINDER HEAD FOR FORD 10, WITH NORMAL
POSITION FOR WATER TAKE OFF. (*Right*) AQUAPLANE ALLOY CYLINDER HEAD
FOR FORD 10, WITH END TAKE-OFF FOR WATER

AQUAPLANE 900/2 S.U.K. MANIFOLD FOR FORD 10, WITH LARGE BORE S.U.
CARBURETTERS

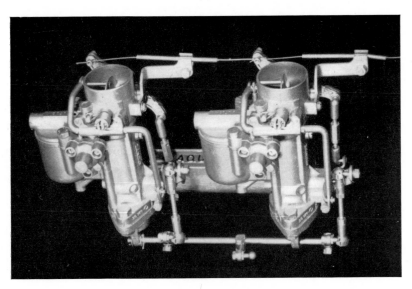

AQUAPLANE MANIFOLD 900/2ZB FOR FORD 10, WITH VIG ZENITH ACCELERATOR-
PUMP CARBURETTERS

AQUAPLANE MANIFOLD 900/2ZK, WITH STANDARD FORD 10 CARBURETTERS

THE $2\frac{1}{2}$-LITRE RILEY ENGINE

1,250-C.C. M.G. TYPE TD ENGINE, OFFSIDE

1,250-C.C. M.G. TYPE TD ENGINE, NEARSIDE

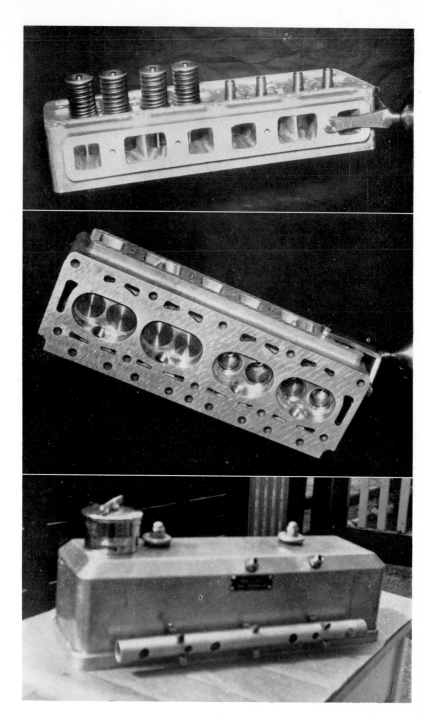

THE AUSTIN A40 EXHIBITION ENGINE, SECTIONED TO SHOW COMPONENTS. THE LAYOUT IS TYPICAL OF THE AUSTIN RANGE

— (*Top and centre*) THE LAYSTALL ALLOY CYLINDER HEAD FOR .G. ENGINES ENHANCES EXTRA PERFORMANCE OBTAINED BY VARIOUS UNING STAGES. (*Bottom*) IMPROVED APPEARANCE OF THE ENGINE ND A DECIDED REDUCTION IN VALVE GEAR NOISE. AN ALLOY OCKER-BOX DESIGN BY THE AUTHOR. NOTE QUICK FILLER AND H.T. CABLE CONDUIT

AN EFFECTIVE FOUR CARBURETTER INDUCTION LAYOUT ON THE 1,100-C.C. RILEY
ENGINE

A RILEY 1,100-C.C. ENGINE FITTED WITH AN EXHAUST SYSTEM WHICH HAS GIVEN
EXCELLENT RESULTS, AND SHOWS EVIDENCE OF CAREFUL PLANNING IN REGARD
TO PIPE DIMENSIONS AND LENGTH

THE DAVIES SPECIAL MANIFOLD FOR THE S.V. MORRIS MINOR WITH TWO
S.U. CARBURETTERS

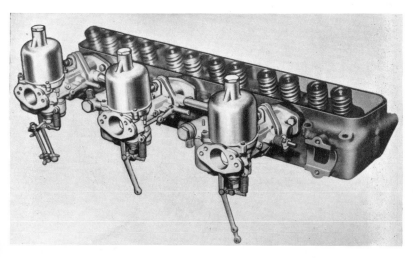

(*Cyril F. Ford, Spalding*)

THE RAYMOND MAYS THREE CARBURETTER INDUCTION SYSTEM FOR
THE FORD "ZEPHYR" ENGINE

THE JOWETT FLAT-FOUR ENGINE

THE SHORROCK SUPERCHARGER INSTALLATION ON THE MARK II O.H.V.   MORRIS
MINOR SHOWING CARBURETTER AND INLET ARRANGEMENT

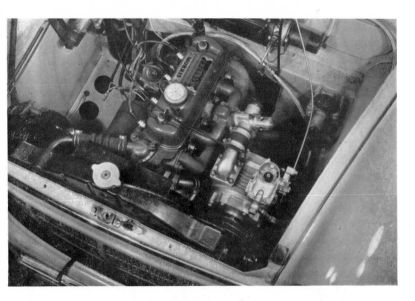

THE SHORROCK SUPERCHARGER INSTALLATION ON THE MARK II O.H.V. 800-C.C. MORRIS MINOR

VIEW SHOWING INTERNAL ARRANGEMENT OF SHORROCK SUPERCHARGER (TYPE C 142B)

THE SHORROCK SUPERCHARGER INSTALLATION ON SERIES M.M. SIDE
VALVE MORRIS MINOR

EXPLODED VIEW OF A WADE BLOWER

THE WADE SUPERCHARGER INSTALLATION FITTED TO AN M.G. TYPE TC ENGINE

192

removing metal. In any case, as has been shown, there is plenty of pressure available to clear the exhaust, and the time factor is ample. In consequence, obstructions in the port which would be a grave disadvantage in the inlet tract are of no consequence as far as the exhaust is concerned.

The exhaust valves have to stand a lot of heat, the bulk of which is dissipated from the valve itself, by conduction through its contact with the guide and seating. The guide should therefore not be shortened, and the seating must remain of ample width. If there is plenty of metal in the guide, it can be streamlined in the direction of gas flow, in the same way as was done for the inlet, but the wall thickness of the guide should be left on the generous side. Regarding the valve, the top edge can be radiused off in the same manner as for the inlet valve, removing only the minimum amount of metal.

Generally, an exhaust valve having a slightly convex head is preferable to a flat one, even though it may be a shade heavier. In view of the heat, it is policy to play safe, particularly when high compression ratios or supercharging is contemplated. For very high outputs, valves of very special alloy steel are obtainable. Sodium-filled or similar types with augmented cooling are available, but are an unnecessary luxury in most cases where sports engines are concerned. In any case, being larger in the stem than the normal valve, special large-bore guides are needed.

There is no benefit in modifying standard exhaust valves in the manner described for inlets, but it is sometimes possible to fit larger ones, the limitations on size having already been mentioned in connection with inlet valves, and being equally applicable. If larger valves are fitted, the ports should be merged into the larger diameter seating, and, of course, if there is sufficient thickness of metal available, the ports can be enlarged right through to the outlet flanges.

Valves, springs and collars

Standard valve guides, modified as already described, will meet most requirements. A very small frictional loss will be

N

saved by using phosphor bronze inlet valve guides, but this metal is unsuitable for exhaust valve guides.

An alloy such as Barronia-metal will serve for both. With this type of guide, ample lubrication is required, but the standard system should provide this without modification, unless it incorporates rather extreme methods of preventing oil from reaching the valve stems, as is sometimes done.

Coil springs are normally standard on engines of the type being considered, and are perfectly satisfactory for r.p.m. in the range to be expected. Enormous spring pressures may feel impressive, but are quite unnecessary, and are very wasteful of power, besides putting undesirable loads on the valve gear. The spring pressure chosen should be only that which is necessary to prevent valve-crash at the maximum revs which it is proposed to use. It should be remembered that at some point there must be a limit to the maximum r.p.m., and it is preferable for valve-crash to set this limit rather than a broken crankshaft.

The specialist valve-spring makers will always advise on spring strength. It is not easy to give any hard and fast rule, the best method being to start with standard springs and if these prove inadequate, to increase the strength by a small amount. At maximum revolutions, the inertia of the valve gear amounts to a considerable load, and this is influenced by such times as valve lift and cam contour. Thus, trial and error gives the only real answer to the question of correct spring strength.

Dual or triple springs will no doubt be standardized, and if these are a push fit within each other, some damping will be provided which prevents coil surging at high revs. This surging, which is a sympathetic vibration of the coils running up and down the length of the spring, can lead to fracture if it reaches excessive proportions.

Any measure which can be taken to lighten the load on the springs and valve operating mechanism is of advantage, since it not only reduces inertia loss and stresses, but increases reliability. Thus, weight reduction of the reciprocating parts should be given careful attention. The valve spring collars will probably be found to have a diameter fully equal to the outside diameter of the outer spring coil. It is quite feasible to turn down the outer diameter of the collar until it is equal to a little over the diameter of the spring coil measured at its mean diameter. Some valves are fitted with a shroud designed to prevent oil from reaching the valve guide to excess, this shroud being located under the collar. With valves and guides in really good order, it is sometimes possible to remove these without excessive plug oiling resulting, but in any case about half the shroud length can be cut off in most cases without detriment to their designed function, this giving a further saving in reciprocating weight.

When a change has been made in valve springs, it is important to check that at maximum lift of the cam, the coils are not closed right up, as such a contingency would throw an impossible strain on the valve gear. There must also be adequate clearance (at least $\frac{1}{8}$ in.) between the top of the valve guide and the spring collar, and if necessary, the top of the guide must be ground to provide this amount. Otherwise, contact may take place should momentary over-revving occur from any cause, and this could be serious if it led to valve-stem breakage.

When finally assembling the valves in the head, they should be ground in, even if new, finishing off with metal polish. Valve stems should be polished with superfine emery cloth, rubbing along the stem and not around it, so as to ease down any turning ridges. After assembly of springs, collars and split-cone cotters, the latter can be checked for correct fitting by a light tap or two on the collar itself.

Exhaust pipe layout

Reference has already been made in Chapter 3 to the importance of exhaust pipe design. A glance at the exhaust systems of many cars competing in speed events, however, shows that, in comparison with their counterparts in the motor-cycle world, comparatively little attention has been given to this important adjunct to the scavenging system.

It is true that freedom of exit for the gases is a desirable feature, but apart from this, the utilization of exhaust pipe energy to the full depends on the correct design of manifolding and piping. In general, there is a good deal of latitude in the design of what may be termed a " good " pipe; that is, the diameter, for example, is not unduly critical within reasonable limits. On the other hand, outside such limits it is easy to stray into the " bad " pipe category, by committing the common fault of making the pipe unduly large in diameter. An outsize pipe is quite likely to be inferior to a standard silencing system in regard to power output.

With a given camshaft, variations in pipe length and diameter will result in more power over a certain range of engine r.p.m., but no more, and possibly less power outside that range. The point to decide, therefore, is where the useful revolution range lies, and to concentrate on designing a pipe which will give the greatest power increase within this range. If the engine is of a type which, with modifications generally as detailed in other chapters, peaks at say 6,000 r.p.m., it is probable that below 3,500 there is only moderate power available, and that in usage the r.p.m. would be kept floating in the 3,500/6,000 r.p.m. range. These figures are quoted just as an example, but there is no difficulty in arriving at the figures for any particular engine.

Whilst the reference is to " designing " a pipe, it has to be recognized that patience is worth much paper work in this connection. The first step is to commence with a pipe of reasonably small diameter. It is remarkable that $1\frac{1}{2}$ to $1\frac{3}{4}$ in. diameter seems to suit such widely differing types of engines as motor-cycle and aircraft types, but such is the case. A start can be made with a $1\frac{3}{4}$-in. pipe on an engine of up to 1,500 c.c. The length should be as short as will allow the gases to be clear of the cockpit, but not carried to the extreme rear. Thus, extension pieces can be added for experiment until the best length is obtained. With data available for different lengths of $1\frac{3}{4}$-in. pipe, a similar process should be undergone with a pipe of $\frac{1}{4}$ in. less diameter.

All the above means hard work, but may well pay dividends in extra m.p.h. for speed events, and is worth the trouble. As regards the actual manifolding, this should comprise pipes from each port, leading with easy sweeps into the main pipe. The exit pipes from the ports should not be too short, and their flanges must mate up with the cylinder ports with the same precision as in the case of the inlet manifold flanges. The main pipe at the section where the separate pipes enter it may be of somewhat larger diameter than the tail-pipe, and special adapter pieces at its exit will enable tail-pipes of different diameter to be fitted for experiment on the aforementioned lines.

On four-cylinder engines operating at very high r.p.m., up to about 7,500, it has been found beneficial to use separate manifolds, one having branches serving cylinders 1–4, and the other serving 2–3. With six-cylinder engines, two three-branch manifolds may similarly be used, serving respectively cylinders 1–2–3 and 4–5–6. It will be obvious that equal spacing of impulses is obtained in each case. Where two manifolds are employed, their outer exits may be connected to a single tail-pipe, but the junction must be very well clear of the manifolds themselves.

CHAPTER 16

Modifications to Valve Gear

Rocker accuracy—Rocker-shaft details—Cam followers—
Modifications to standard timing—Lightening tappets

Rocker accuracy

In the case of engines having push-rod- and rocker-operated o.h. valves, there is quite a lot that can be done to increase reliability and, by reducing inertia, to obtain a gain in mechanical efficiency. If the rocker-shaft and rockers are temporarily assembled, in the same condition as when removed from the head, it will be possible to check how the rockers meet the valve stems, since the length of the latter exert quite a large influence, and this length is subject to alteration whenever the valves are ground or their seats recut.

The ideal is, of course, that with the valve in the half-lift position, a line drawn through the rocker, and making a right-angle with a line drawn through the valve-stem axis, should run just across the tip of the valve stem. Further, the rocker tip should contact the valve stem exactly at its central axis. It will be appreciated that the tip of the rocker actually slides across the end of the valve stem during movement of the valve from open to closed and vice versa, and this movement can set up an appreciable side-thrust on the stem unless the dimension referred to is correct.

In a comparatively little-used engine there should be small grounds for criticism, but in cases where the valve-seats have been recut or otherwise received attention, it is probable that the measurements will require attention. If the valve-stem is too long, a little can be ground off the end, taking care to keep everything absolutely square. Alternatively, it may be possible to pack up the rocker-shaft standards to increase the height of the rocker fulcrum, but this may lead to complications with the push-rod length.

If the valve-stem is too short, the rocker-shaft standards

may be lowered to correspond, by machining some metal off their lower faces so as to bring the rockers into the correct position. This may involve shortening the push-rods, but it is probable that the available adjustment at the push-rod end of the rocker will be sufficient to get everything correct.

Another method of compensating for a too-short valve stem is to fit a hardened-steel cap over the end of the stem, but this means a loose component, which is undesirable, as well as adding weight to the valve.

Reduction of friction in the valve-gear is well worth while. It is true that the power loss from this cause is insignificant compared with general frictional losses inside the engine. On the other hand, it should be remembered that the return motion of the valves is dependent on spring pressure and nothing else, and at high revolutions there is not much margin of spring strength to overcome the inertia effect of the operating gear. This does not apply at lower r.p.m. when inertia is small, but as the speed rises there is progressively less margin of spring energy available to keep the valves following the cams. Thus, if any improvement can be effected which will reduce frictional and inertia losses, it means that the valve timing will be adhered to over a higher range of revolutions, and reliability will be increased.

Rocker-shaft details

The rockers should be quite free on their shaft, but without shake. The standard bushes should meet this requirement very well, and last a long time. Coil-spring separators are very frequently used between adjacent rockers, the slight stiffness imparted to the rocker movement by these being considered to have a silencing effect. It is doubtful if this is really considerable, and the friction is much better eliminated. The springs should therefore be replaced by tubular distance-pieces of mild steel or, better still, phosphor-bronze. These must be very carefully dimensioned to bring each rocker over its valve-stem in the correct position, and allow just sufficient end movement to give free operation. This end-play should be tested repeatedly until it is correct, as the act of tightening-down the rocker-shaft standards to the head may cause a reduction in end-play which must be allowed for in the final assembly. Liability to tightening-up due to heat expansion should also be borne in mind. Too much side-play must be avoided at all costs.

The mass of metal present in the modern rough-finished rocker will give rise to thoughts on the possibility of carrying out lightening operations. If such work is done, it must be carried out scientifically, as the component is very highly stressed. Rigidity is the first requirement, as flexure of rockers will permit a valve timing very different from what the designer intended.

If the rocker is considered as a beam which rocks about a fulcrum approximately at its centre it will be seen that the loading is roughly greatest close to the fulcrum and decreases progressively towards the ends of the beam. Many types of rocker lie at an angle to the rocker-shaft in plan view, so that the fulcrum is subjected to twisting as well as bending. Thus, the centre of the rocker is obviously the part where liberties must not be taken, but this part also moves at the lowest speed, while the lightly loaded extremities move at the highest speed. Lightening should therefore be concentrated at the points where stresses are low. Starting with the push-rod end of the rocker, it may be found possible to reduce the length of the adjusting screw projecting above the rocker, and also the size of the locknut. It is also practicable in some cases to grind an appreciable amount of metal off the rocker end contacting the valve stem. This should be removed from the sides, and not from the working face. A very small amount of metal may also be removed from the sides of the rockers throughout their length, but if there is any doubt about the wisdom of such a step, leave well alone. In any case, the depth should not be interfered with, as it is this dimension which primarily resists the bending stresses. When it is finally decided that the rockers are as light as possible they should be polished all over, using any means available. This polishing is a most valuable bar to fatigue failure.

The rocker-shaft should be tested for parallelism, first by rolling it on a flat surface and then with a straight-edge. The shaft must be absolutely rigid in its supports, the latter being usually bolted to the head, though sometimes studs and nuts are used. Either type of fixing should incorporate high-tensile material. It is normal practice to lock the rocker-standard bolts by thin steel locking-plates or spring washers. A sounder method is to drill the bolt-heads and use locking-wire. This facilitates removal of the components and cuts out the need for hammer and punch operations on the plates, which is always liable to result in chips of metal breaking off.

The standard push-rods are usually of high-tensile steel tubing, and are capable of standing a considerable increase in loading without failure. They should be perfectly straight, and can be tested in the same manner as was done for the rocker shaft. If it is desired to experiment with alloy push-rods duralumin tubing to specification 4T4 may be used. The diameter should be on the generous side, say $\frac{3}{8}$ in., with wall thickness corresponding to 16 S.W.G. This will give an internal diameter suitable for receiving the end-fittings, which obviously must be really tight, as they cannot be sweated in place. The push-rods, of whatever material, should be polished all over.

Cam followers

Cam followers used with some types of o.h.c. engines can be dealt with as described for normal o.h.v. rockers, as regards lightening, polishing, and so on. Worn or scored followers can be built up and re-ground to shape if new ones are unobtainable, but care must be taken to ensure that the original contours are not lost. Drawings or templates are usually available giving the original shape, and the work must be checked against these, as some specialists in this type of job appear to adopt a standard shape for the wearing surface, irrespective of the make.

Modifications to standard timing

As far as modifications to standard valve timing are concerned, it will be obvious that such alterations constitute a major item, and that there is much that can be done to enhance the performance of an engine without recourse to a special camshaft. It is usual for sports engines to employ valve timing which gives a good all-round performance fairly high up in the engine speed range, possibly at the sacrifice of some torque at low r.p.m. This is generally evident by the degree of overlap at exhaust t.d.c. As far as these engines are concerned, therefore, the standard camshaft will meet most requirements. Some makers provide alternative camshafts for special applications, such as sports-car racing, but these, of course, have their disadvantages at normal speeds.

Sports engines usually have considerable rocker clearance, particularly push-rod o.h.v. types, thus enabling cams to be used which give a relatively slow take-up of clearances, after which a quick valve-lift is obtained. The cams are designed so that the lift commences at a slow rate several degrees before the point at which, with all clearances taken up, the valve opens. This method reduces the valve-gear loading and makes for comparatively quick operation. Although it would appear that the opening period of the valve can be extended if desired by reducing the clearance, this is fallacious, since with less than the designed clearance, the inertia at high speeds would actually cause the valve to " float " open much longer than intended. In fact, it is usual to increase the already large clearance, on many engines of this type, for extra-high-speed operation.

The normal engine is equipped for road use with a silencer, and the cam design is determined having regard to the fact that a silencer will be used. With a free exhaust, it is usually possible to enhance performance without alteration to the timing. However, for the benefit of those who wish to experiment, it may be stated that with a completely open exhaust some extension to both the opening periods and overlap can usually be allowed, which will give a considerable increase in torque at the upper end of the power curve. The performance with silencer, and lower down the r.p.m. range will, however, be adversely affected.

With a spare camshaft available, a modification can be made to the standard cams to give a special timing. The cams, being hardened, will stand having, say, up to .025 in. ground off the base, where the loading is negligible, and still leave sufficient wearing depth. This reduction in the base circle diameter will naturally have the effect of increasing the maximum lift, with standard clearances. At the same time, by suitably blending the new base circle into the flanks of the cam, the opening period can be extended to any desired degree.

The modification requires rather special equipment to carry out satisfactorily, but it may be useful to some readers to go further into the matter.

The shape of the standard cams must first be obtained, together with the centre-point. From the latter, the base circle radius can be ascertained. If it is proposed to remove, say, .025 in. from the base circle, the revised radius must be drawn inside the existing one. It will now be possible to see just what happens to the valve " lift " and " lower " points where they join the new base circle. It is, of course, essential that the cam contours are blended smoothly into the new base circle as otherwise noise and undesirably heavy loading will be set up to no purpose, but by comparing the existing timing diagram and cam contour with the proposed modified cam, it should be easy to find the best shape to give the required increase in lift, duration of opening, and overlap.

As regards the actual amount by which the opening periods should be increased there is obviously no point in going to the trouble of making a special camshaft unless fairly drastic alterations are made to the timing.

Assuming the use of a straight-through exhaust, and with the emphasis on high revolutions, it should be possible to increase the opening by a percentage amount equal to the percentage increase in maximum r.p.m. For example, if it is decided that the engine can peak at 6,000 instead of 5,500 r.p.m., representing an increase in r.p.m. of 9 per cent., and the existing inlet opening period is 250 deg., this should be also increased by 9 per cent., making the new opening period 275 deg. The exhaust opening is dealt with in the same manner, and the overlap period is naturally increased automatically. As an initial venture, it is suggested that the increase is made equally, half on either side of the existing opening period. The work must be done very accurately, on a grinder with the proper type of attachments. The final blending is done by hand, with an oil-stone.

Lightening tappets

So much for camshaft modifications. The associated items, i.e., tappets or cam-plungers, can in some cases be lightened considerably without impairing their strength or wearing qualities. In the case of tappets of the usual barrel type, the diameter in the centre can often be reduced, leaving the full diameter at the top and lower ends so that only these portions rest on the guide. The load is, of course, heaviest at the ends, the centre part taking little load.

CHAPTER 17

Attention to Cylinders and Pistons

*Exacting clearances—Piston rings—Gas leakage—Piston design—
Connecting rods—Correcting errors*

Exacting clearances

The cylinders and pistons comprise the most important components in the engine. Piston friction accounts for a very large percentage of the total frictional loss, while the pistons themselves operate under conditions of high and varying speeds and temperatures. In addition to performing its main function of taking the expansion pressure and transmitting it to the connecting rod, the piston has also to act as an efficient pump plunger, and at the same time to resist the connecting rod side thrust. Obviously, therefore, every component must be in perfect order in this department, if the engine is to respond to attention of the kind with which this book is concerned.

As regards wear, while we are not primarily dealing with overhauling matters, some brief details will be useful. The maximum amount of wear occurs at the top of the ring travel, while just above the bottom of the stroke the bore remains about the original diameter, even in a well-worn engine.

Wear up to approximately .007 in. in cylinders of a diameter up to 3-in. bore does not impair performance to a very marked degree, providing that the bore surfaces are in good condition. Excessive oil consumption can often be checked, up to this limit of wear, by fitting new rings. Greater amounts of wear are usually only corrected by reboring or the fitting of liners.

Pistons which have been running correctly will show a perfectly even bearing surface over the thrust faces, without any highly polished areas denoting excessive rubbing contact. Obviously, such areas will not be present if the piston clearance is excessive, but this fault will show up by the presence of brown patches of carbon deposit on the non-thrust sides of the skirt, and also by evidence of heavy loading at top and bottom, denoting tilting.

Providing the general clearances are in order, a few odd high spots can usually be eased. The important thing is to differentiate between genuine high spots and normal running contact areas, and this is not always easy. Usually, normal loading produces a smooth, dullish finish, while high spots are quite highly polished and may even be scored if momentary seizure has taken place. If any such high spots are present, they must be eased down very carefully with a smooth file, taking care not to overdo this operation, as it is fatally easy to remove too much metal.

In regard to actual running clearances, it is nearly always best to adhere to the makers' recommendations. It is sometimes thought that sloppy and noisy pistons are no disadvantage on a high-speed engine, on the score of reduced friction and the ability to deal with the extra degree of expansion of the metal called for by added heat flow. In actual fact, using fuel correct for the compression ratio employed, the increase in piston temperature is not very great, and is easily catered for by an additional clearance of one or two " thous " over the standard clearance. In other words, a very small amount of bore wear will more than compensate for this extra heat expansion.

Piston rings

Piston rings in normal fitting are occasionally treated in a rather casual manner, but for maximum efficiency a good deal of care can profitably be expended when assembling them. The main function of the rings is to curtail leakage past the piston. It is, of course, not possible to stop all leakage completely, as in such a case the friction set up would be much worse in its effect on the mechanical efficiency than the power loss arising from the leakage. However, the leakage can be reduced to the unavoidable minimum by careful fitting. The three possible leakage paths are through the ring gap, around the back of the ring, and past the face of the ring.

Gap leakage was at one time thought to be the biggest offender, and many tuners went to great lengths to reduce the gap to very small amounts, often with dire results. Ring makers, for their part, produced rings with stepped and other peculiar gap shapes. Research has since effectively shown that gaps of even 1/16 in. allow little leakage. Regarding leakage around the back of the ring, it will be appreciated that it is necessary to allow a clearance of about .002 to .003 in. between the side of the ring and the groove, so that the ring can spring quite freely. Thus when the piston is moving upwards on the exhaust stroke, the ring is forced against the lower face of the groove because of its own inertia and its friction against the cylinder. This close contact between ring and groove closes the leakage path round the back of the ring. In the same way, when the piston is moving downwards on the inlet stroke, the ring is held against the upper face of the ring groove. During the compression and expansion strokes, the ring is held by gas pressure against the bottom face. Thus, the seal can only be effective if the sides of the ring and the groove faces are really accurate, and the ring-to-groove clearance is correct. Damage to the groove faces must be avoided when fitting or removing rings, as the contact should be akin to that of a valve and its seat.

Gas leakage

Leakage across the ring face increases with wear, particularly as the bore does not wear truly circular, so that the radial pressure on the ring must be able to accommodate, to some extent, variations in this respect. At the same time, excessive radial pressure will produce too high a frictional loss.

When a considerable increase in r.p.m. is being considered, it is a good plan to consult the piston ring makers regarding choice of rings, since it is possible for a sudden increase in blow-by to take place above a certain critical speed. Various theories have been put forward to account for this, one of the most feasible being that at very high speeds the inertia of the ring is sufficient to lift it off its contact face with the side of the groove on the compression and exhaust strokes. This action allows escape of pressure round the back of the ring, so that gas pressure, which should be augmenting the natural spring of the ring in maintaining the seal against the cylinder wall, is relieved, and the ring collapses inwards. Then, leakage takes place across its face. If the ring gap is too small, actual ring breakage can result due to the ends butting.

When fitting rings, a proper expanding tool should be used which not only ensures that the ends of the ring are kept parallel, but prevents the piston skirt and grooves from becoming scratched. The side clearance already mentioned must be present between the ring and groove, and if it is necessary to increase the clearance, one side only of the ring must be rubbed down on a sheet of fine emery cloth placed on a perfectly flat surface, such as plate-glass. The ring can be finished off with metal polish on the glass. When fitting the ring, the face treated thus should bear against the upper face of the groove, so that the untouched face is against the lower groove. This will ensure that the best seal takes place on the compression and firing strokes. The rings should be gapped to between .003 and .005 in. per in. of cylinder diameter.

The usual type of rectangular-section ring acts to some extent as an oil-control ring in addition to its main function, but is not usually sufficiently effective in this capacity to obviate the use of oil-control rings. The usual design of the latter, or scraper ring, as it is often called, relies on a suitable grading of its pressure against the bore to remove the desired amount of oil. The amount of pressure is determined by the contact area of the ring against the bore, and is of the order of 100 lb. per sq. in. The oil thus removed is transferred to the inside of the piston via suitable ducts. This is the general principle, but different designs vary in minor details.

The scraper rings are placed below the compression rings, and it is important that while they are sufficiently effective to prevent excessive oil consumption, they are not so drastic in action as to cause the bores to run dry as this will result in excessive friction and a high rate of wear. Many standard engines are excessively " dry " rather than the reverse, but for high-speed operation it is wise to err, if at all, on the side of under-scraping, i.e., to reduce the ring pressure.

Piston design

For normal increases in performance, the makers' standard pistons can usually cope with the extra mechanical and thermal stresses. These are generally of the cast type, which have been universally employed for many years. For very arduous conditions, forged pistons have come to the fore in some cases, but apart from their expense it will be realized that the internal shape is dictated largely by machining considerations. The forged piston must be machined both externally and internally, being usually made, in the small sizes concerned, from solid bar material.

Since both forged and cast pistons are made from the same sort of material, with substantially the same melting point, it might be queried why the former resist trouble better than the cast type. The point is that with cast material, the tensile strength of the metal is reduced with heat to a greater extent than is the case with forged material. A melted piston crown usually starts with a crack, the edges of which fuse and accelerate the growth of the " hole." The forged piston is better able to resist cracking in the first place. However, in view of the strides made recently in cast piston manufacture, there is little likelihood of failure of the type, if clearances and fitting are correct. Piston makers are able to cover all requirements, and their choice of material can be accepted with confidence.

Connecting rods

Connecting rods are usually made of high-grade steel, and are capable of withstanding a big load increase without failure, as far as competition-type engines are concerned. With touring-type power units, some care is necessary in deciding how far it is safe to go in respect of increased r.p.m. and working pressures. If there is any doubt about the ability of the standard rods to stand up, it is advisable to investigate the possibility of obtaining replacement rods of higher-grade material.

Another profitable line of investigation is the use of lighter rods, since any reduction in reciprocating weight means less stress and greater reliability. It is definitely not advisable to carry out any lightening operations on standard rods unless the risk of an expensive blow-up is accepted, but it is possible to obtain for some engines light-alloy rods which provide a strength-weight ratio equal to, or greater than, the original rod.

The importance of parallelism of big and little end bearing eyes will be obvious. This can be checked by the use of ground steel mandrels and vee-blocks together with a surface

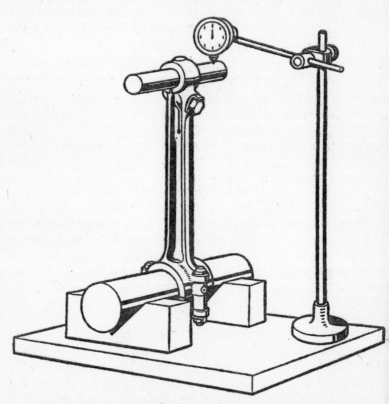

CHECKING THE CONNECTING ROD FOR ALIGNMENT. THE INDICATOR DIAL SHOULD GIVE THE SAME READING AT EACH END OF THE TEST BAR CLAMPED IN THE LITTLE END

plate and dial gauge, as shown in the illustrations herewith. The dial gauge is used for checking alignment, the rod being rested vertically in two vee-blocks carrying the big-end mandrel. The gauge is applied to each end of the little-end mandrel. If the mandrels are about 8 in. long, and projecting equally on either side of the rod, a difference of .002 in. in gauge reading between each end is permissible.

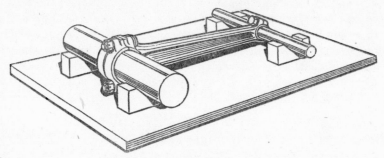

TESTING THE CONNECTING ROD FOR TWIST

For checking twist, four vee-blocks are used, the rod being supported horizontally on the two mandrels, which rest on the blocks. There should be no rock or movement perceptible, i.e., each mandrel end must rest firmly in contact with its block.

Correcting errors

Any errors which are discovered as a result of either of these tests can be corrected by hand, providing they are only slight. A large vice, and two long mandrels to fit the bearing eyes are necessary, the mandrel length being such as to give adequate leverage. When applying pressure to correct the error, care must be taken not to introduce another fault. For example, in correcting twist in the rod, the bearings might easily be put out of parallel. Before starting operations, therefore, it is necessary to weigh up carefully what is required. Twist is not difficult to correct as there is the whole length of rod to accommodate this. Lack of parallelism of bearings is not so easy, as the rod may tend to bend at one point only because of its shape. If the force is applied a little at a time, checking at frequent intervals, the results will be good.

Polishing of connecting rods is a worth-while luxury, and, of course, increases resistance to fatigue. The amount of hard work may be lessened by recourse to mechanical aids. When carrying out this operation, the rods should also be checked for weight against each other. There may be an appreciable degree of latitude on a production engine in this respect, but if in cleaning up the rods a little superfluous metal is removed (at rough edges, for example), this can be used to correct any errors in relative weights. The rods should therefore be weighed before commencing polishing, the lightest rod being finished off first. The others can then be finished to that weight.

CHAPTER 18

Choice of Compression Ratio

Raising the ratio—Obtaining head volume—Valve clearance—Special pistons—
The cylinder-head joint

Raising the ratio

The question of raising the compression ratio probably gives rise to more arguments and misunderstandings than any other aspect of engine tuning. It is, of course, a fairly simple operation to carry out, and the results in many cases are disappointing, merely because of an insufficient appreciation of all the factors involved.

We have seen from Chapter 1 the theory underlying the influence of comp. r. on the thermal efficiency, but we have also noted that the theory assumes conditions of breathing which do not obtain in practice. The absolute pressure at the end of the compression stroke depends not only on the comp. r., but also on the pressure existing at the start of the stroke, and this in turn depends on how much mixture has been inhaled, i.e., on the volumetric efficiency. Obviously, if the mixture at the end of the induction stroke is " rarefied," as it were, a high comp. r. will only provide the same final compression pressure as would obtain with a well-filled cylinder and a moderate comp. r. Further, a combustion chamber design which does not promote rapid burning, but leaves pockets of stagnant mixture, may well stand a higher comp. r. than one which gives clean and complete combustion. These statements will be obvious after a study of foregoing chapters, but are worth stressing.

However, there is little doubt that almost any engine designed to operate passably well on pool fuel will benefit from a change to premium brands and an increase in compression ratio, if this can be achieved without mechanical complications. Most engines have to be designed on the basis that a percentage of thoughtless individuals will use cheap and nasty fuel, but many makers nowadays offer alternative compression ratios, and specify the fuel to be used, this being true in particular of manufacturers of sports-type power units.

As a very rough guide, the increase, in the case of side-valve or push-rod o.h.v. engines, can be in the neighbourhood of " one ratio," i.e., from, say, 7 : 1 to 8 : 1, if a change of fuel is made from the equivalent of pool to premium. Some engines with really efficient cooling will stand appreciably higher ratios without distress, but in all cases it is necessary to check that adequate clearances are maintained internally, and that the combustion chamber shape does not suffer as a result of machining operations.

A remarkably reliable guide to the compression ratio which it is feasible to use with any given fuel can be stated. If the individual area of one piston does not exceed 8.5 sq. in. and the combustion chamber is of a good shape, of orthodox pattern, a comp. r. of 10 per cent. of the octane rating of the fuel will be about right. For example, with fuel of 72 octane, the comp. r. would be 7.2 : 1. If 80 octane is available, this can be raised to 8 : 1. For combustion chambers of really excellent characteristics half-a-ratio higher is quite permissible.

The above piston area represents a bore of about 80 mm., so that the rule is applicable to virtually all engines with which we are concerned.

Obtaining head volume

In order to determine the amount of metal to be removed from the head surface to obtain any desired comp. r., it is necessary to obtain the volume of the combustion chamber when the piston is at t.d.c. Due to the irregular shape of the chamber, any attempt to determine the volume by linear measurement is out of the question. However, it is not a difficult matter to measure by means of liquid introduced into the combustion chamber, with the head upside down on the bench and held absolutely level. The valves should, of course, be in position, and closed, and the plug orifice suitably sealed. The liquid used may be paraffin or water, and this is run in from a burette until its level is flush with the face of the head. (See illustration, page 215.)

The volume thus obtained is that of the standard head, and, in conjunction with the swept volume of one cylinder, will give the comp. r. by use of the normal formula (given in Appendix I). The decreased head volume necessary for the higher ratio can be determined also from the formula, and when this has been obtained it is necessary to measure the revised quantity of liquid into the combustion chamber. Its level will naturally be slightly below the machined face, and this " high-water mark " must be carefully scribed on the chamber wall to show the amount of metal which has to be machined off.

If any measurements appear in the least doubtful, as for

LIQUID

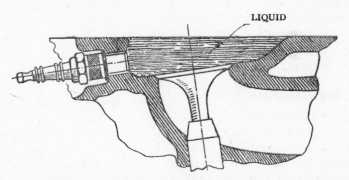

MEASUREMENT OF COMBUSTION CHAMBER VOLUME BY QUANTITY OF LIQUID

example, if the level seems to call for an unduly large amount of metal to be removed for the ratio chosen, a careful check must be made. The need for the head to be absolutely flat during these operations must be stressed. A large vice and a spirit level are essential items of equipment.

It will be realized that in arriving at the head volume in the above manner, no account has been taken of the capacity taken up by the cylinder head gasket, which will add something due to its thickness. This small amount is added whether the head is modified or not, and in practice makes little difference. If it is desired to calculate the " volume " taken up, the swept volume formula (given in Appendix I) may be used, using the cylinder bore and gasket thickness dimensions in either inches or millimetres. This will be sufficiently

accurate, though, of course, in many engines the gasket
aperture is not truly circular.

Having marked the combustion chamber wall as described,
the distance from the marking to the head face can readily be
measured by calipers and a rule. Before commencing
machining operations, a thorough examination should be
made to determine whether there are any structural or
mechanical snags to be expected. In some cases the spark
plug aperture will be fairly near the faced joint, and machining
the face may actually bring it right down to the joint. This
does not matter providing the gasket is well back, and does
not protrude into the combustion chamber when the plug
orifice has been faired off by filing. There should be at
least 3/32 in. of flat face between the gasket edge and the
plug orifice edge. The bottom threads of the latter must not
be left ragged after machining the face, but should be filed
and blended into the surrounding metal.

Valve clearance

As regards valve-to-piston clearance, there should be no
difficulty in the case of bath-tub or similar heads where the
valves work more or less vertically, and normal flat-top
pistons are used. In the case of inclined valves, however, the
lower edge of the valve head may be undesirably close to the
piston at maximum lift, and this could also apply to any
o.h.v. engine if special humped pistons are fitted. In such
cases it is necessary to make up a jig comprising a packing
piece which enters the combustion chamber to an extent equal
to the amount of metal it is proposed to remove. The head
is then rested on a flat surface, the correct way up, with the
packing piece in position, and both valves in place, less springs
or other fittings. The valves are then allowed to drop until
their heads touch the packing piece; this position can be said
to approximate to that obtained with the valves touching
the piston. Measure the distance from the end of the valve
stem to the top of the guide in this position, and measure from
the same point with the valve on its seat. The difference
should be not less than 3/16 in., and if this amount is available, it can safely be said that there will be ample clearance
under any operating conditions that can be reasonably

expected with valve timing something near normal. It will be appreciated, of course, that under running conditions, neither valve is fully open at t.d.c., except in very special cases.

Special pistons

If special domed or humped pistons are being considered for very high increases in compression ratio, the above check can be carried out similarly, but using a packing piece with a shape similar to that of the proposed piston crown.

It is probable that a compression ratio enabling the best to be got out of premium grades of fuel will suffice for most competition car owners, and in such cases it is not usually necessary to resort to special pistons of the aforementioned type. If, however, the use of alcohol-based or similar fuel is being contemplated (and as a rough figure a comp. r. of about 9 : 1 will require such fuel) special pistons may be necessary.

They should not be used if machining the head will meet the requirements. Any form of dome or hump on the piston crown is undesirable from the point of view of combustion chamber shape, and in extreme cases can actually hinder the flame path at the moment of ignition. This applies particularly to bath-tub heads, which obviously require a peculiar shape of special piston, but which fortunately can achieve quite high compression ratios without it.

Hemispherical heads, on the other hand, usually need domed pistons for any really appreciable increase, but the clean head shape and position of the plug on this type of engine make the use of these of little disadvantage unless the bore-stroke ratio is such that a very high dome is required.

The cylinder-head joint

Machining the head face for compression ratio modification is quite a straightforward workshop task, and most small machine-shops possess equipment capable of meeting the required standards of accuracy. As regards the joint between block and head, it is considered that for all normal competition purposes there is little to beat the standard gasket, bearing in mind that the head may require to be removed quickly on occasions when the standard of cleanliness may not be all that could be desired. Under such circumstances, a gas-and watertight seal will still be obtained. Metal-to-metal lapped joints, on the other hand, will have their " fit " destroyed by the merest speck of grit, and assembly is at all times a matter for the utmost precision. Some of the special thin gaskets now obtainable are of value in assisting heat conductivity, as well as achieving a small increase in compression ratio without machining operations.

CHAPTER 19

Tuning the Ford Ten

An attractive engine—" Aquaplane " modifications—Tuning in six stages—
Racing equipment—Specialists' recommendations—Volumetric efficiency—
Ignition equipment—Sprint racing

An attractive engine

In Chapter 10, dealing with the design and construction of the 1,172-c.c. Ford engine, mention was made of the very wide popularity of this unit for all forms of competition work, and of the greatly increased power outputs which it is possible to obtain by the use of special fittings and attention to detail.

In the next few pages will be found very full particulars of special components obtainable for this engine, and also the recommendations of well-known Ford enthusiasts in regard to tuning operations.

" Aquaplane " modifications

The Aquaplane Company, of Oulton Broad, Suffolk, have specialized for some time in the manufacture and supply of special fittings for competition purposes for the Ford Ten. Their wealth of experience has resulted in the formulation of a concise and easily followed tuning sequence. Dynamometer tests have proved conclusively the value of the various modifications and special parts.

For easy reference, a list of the more specialized fittings is given later in this chapter, but as this is being added to at frequent intervals, enthusiasts working on these engines are recommended to consult the company for the latest information.

It will be of interest to detail one or two of the more prominent items. The cylinder heads, for example, are made in aluminium alloy, with water spaces specially designed to ensure uniform cooling, and internally ribbed for rigidity.

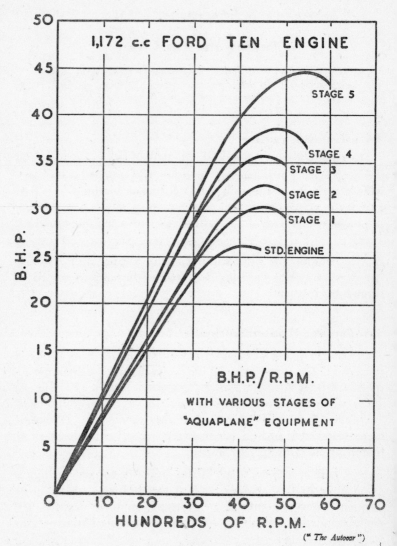

POWER CURVES OF 1,172-C.C. FORD ENGINE WITH VARIOUS STAGES OF
AQUAPLANE EQUIPMENT

Provision is made for a thermometer fitting, and as will be seen from the list, various compression ratios can be catered for up to a maximum of 11 : 1. The weight is a mere 7 lb.

The fitting of special camshafts is frowned on by certain racing regulations, but somewhat naturally the standard camshaft has a limiting effect at a certain stage of tuning. The racing camshaft which is available provides a much different timing, prolonging the power curve in the right direction at higher r.p.m., and in addition, gives a higher lift than standard. For use with this camshaft, valves with lengthened stems are necessary.

An aluminium alloy timing case cover complete with tachometer drive is another useful accessory, the tachometer for use with this having a 4-in. dial, and reading to 7,000 r.p.m. When fitted, this item will fall foul of the dynamo belt, with the dynamo in its standard position. As pointed out later, however, it is good practice to remove the dynamo to another position on a tuned engine. If this is impracticable for any reason (and it should not be), the belt can be made to clear by using a smaller crankshaft pulley.

Tuning in six stages

In giving stage-by-stage modification particulars below, the b.h.p. figures to be expected are included. These may be compared with the figures obtained by test of an " average " standard engine on the same dynamometer, as follows:—

19.6 b.h.p. at 2,500 r.p.m.
23.5   „   3,000   „
25.5   „   3,500   „
26.2   „   4,000   „
21.6   „   4,500   „

Stage 1

This modification comprises the substitution of a type 2VZ twin-carburetter induction manifold for the existing one. On the new manifold are mounted the existing carburetter and a second identical instrument. Thus modified, the following performance is obtained:—

$$19.6 \text{ b.h.p. at } 2,500 \text{ r.p.m.}$$
$$24.2 \quad ,, \quad 3,000 \quad ,,$$
$$27.3 \quad ,, \quad 3,500 \quad ,,$$
$$29.4 \quad ,, \quad 4,000 \quad ,,$$
$$30.4 \quad ,, \quad 4,500 \quad ,,$$
$$29.0 \quad ,, \quad 5,000 \quad ,,$$

The parts required to cover the above are the type 2VZ manifold and the second carburetter. (A detailed list of parts is given later.) Note also the illustration on page 182.

Stage 2

For this modification, the induction manifold as for Stage 1 is fitted, with two Zenith VIG-type carburetters mounted thereon. These instruments are larger than the standard type, the greater choke area giving a b.h.p. increase of about 2 at the top end of the power curve. The carburetters are also fitted with accelerator-pumps, and thus a general improvement in acceleration can be expected. The standard valve springs should be replaced with the racing type, in view of the maintained power at high revolutions.

The parts required for the above comprise the 2VZ manifold, a set of racing valve springs, and two Zenith VIG-type carburetters with fuel pipes and throttle linkage.

In the case of both Stage 1 and Stage 2 modifications, a further performance improvement will result from the fitting of a special exhaust manifold, part No. 1400, as illustrated on page 180.

Stage 2a

This stage of tuning involves the fitting of two S.U. carburetters of large-bore pattern, carried on a 2-carburetter manifold type 2 S.U. The exhaust manifold part, No. 1400, may also be fitted. The performance to be expected will be similar to that obtained from Stage 2.

Stage 3

Fittings as for Stage 1 are employed, plus the replacing of the existing cylinder head by an alloy racing head having combustion chamber volumes graded for operation on 50/50 petrol-benzole fuel or similar.   Using this fuel, the following performance should be expected:—

24.0 b.h.p. at	2,500	r.p.m.
29.4 ,,	3,000	,,
33.5 ,,	3,500	,,
34.5 ,,	4,000	,,
35.5 ,,	4,500	,,
33.5 ,,	5,000	,,

For sustained high revolutions, the racing valve springs should also be fitted in place of the existing ones.

The parts required thus comprise those for Stage 1, together with alloy cylinder head, and racing valve springs (if these are to be fitted).

Two larger Zenith carburetters, type VIG, can be mounted on the manifold, in which case the power output will be:—

24.0 b.h.p. at	2,500	r.p.m.
29.5 ,,	3,000	,,
33.5 ,,	3,500	,,
35.5 ,,	4,000	,,
37.0 ,,	4,500	,,
34.5 ,,	5,000	,,

Again in the above case, a performance increase may be expected by using the exhaust manifold part No. 1400. Spark plugs of Lodge make, type RL 47, should be installed.

Stage 4

In this case, the details are as for Stage 3, but in addition the manifold type 2 S.U. is fitted, complete with two large-bore S.U.-Aquaplane carburetters. The special exhaust manifold is also installed, and racing valve springs are essential. Plugs should be Lodge RL 47 or RL 49. Using 50/50 petrol-benzole, the following performance will be available:—

24.0 b.h.p. at 2,500 r.p.m.
29.5 ,, 3,000 ,,
33.5 ,, 3,500 ,,
36.0 ,, 4,000 ,,
37.0 ,, 4,500 ,,
38.2 ,, 5,000 ,,
33.0 ,, 5,500 ,,

Additional power can be obtained from the above Stage by careful attention to ports and so on, as detailed in Chapter 15. A still higher comp. r. using special racing fuel will also help, but in regard to this it will be appreciated that the standard camshaft restricts the potentialities to a considerable extent.

The components required for Stage 4 are the manifold with two S.U.-Aquaplane carburetters; exhaust manifold No. 1400 ; racing cylinder head and C. & A. gasket, and set of racing valve springs. The power-weight ratio of the engine may be further improved by the use of lightweight racing fittings as listed on page 226.

Stage 5

This stage of tuning gets over the limitations of the standard camshaft by using a racing camshaft and lengthened valves. The valve port sizes must be increased to the maximum possible, or alternatively a " tuned " cylinder block can be obtained with this work done. As r.p.m. up to 6,000 is catered for by these modifications, it is necessary for the rotating parts to be dynamically balanced, while for sustained high speed a high-capacity oil pump must be installed. A racing cylinder head, graded for maximum compression ratio with Aquaplane SRF–30 racing fuel, is fitted, together with a racing gasket. To improve water circulation, an impeller

may be added. Plugs required are Lodge RL 47 or RL 49.
The following power can be expected:—

24.5 b.h.p. at 2,500 r.p.m.

33.0	,,	3,000	,,
36.6	,,	3,500	,,
40.0	,,	4,000	,,
42.5	,,	4,500	,,
44.0	,,	5,000	,,
44.5	,,	5,500	,,
43.0	,,	6,000	,,

The components required comprise inlet and exhaust
manifolds and carburetters as for Stage 4; racing cylinder
head and gasket; racing camshaft, set of lengthened valves,
and racing valve springs; oil pressure adjuster; high capacity
oil pump ; lightened and balanced flywheel; water impeller.

Stage 6

For extreme performance, particularly acceleration, in the
hands of experts, the " super-light " flywheel weighing 4 lb.
2 oz. will assist considerably, and in addition, the power-weight
ratio can be further improved by using other alloy components. Thus, to the Stage 5 parts should be added the
super-light alloy flywheel, and the alloy water impeller,
timing case cover, and valve chest cover. For the extreme
in r.p.m.—7,000 or more, precision of ignition is assured by
fitting a high-speed distributor unit and racing battery.

It is pointed out that, at all events for the later stages of
tuning, it is not good practice to retain the standard dynamo
mounting on the cylinder head, or indeed to " tack " any
other accessories on to the engine in this way. A dynamo
support incorporated in the front engine bearer can be
obtained, or made up, and in the case of the one supplied by
Aquaplane, the water impeller also is accommodated.

Aquaplane Racing Equipment—Alphabetical List

Item.	Part No.
Adaptor, manifold (see manifold)	—
Adaptor, centre water outlet, cyl. head	12
Battery, special racing	950/8
Balancing, flywheel and crankshaft	—
Cylinder head, racing and super-sports. Comp. r. up to 11 to 1. Aluminium alloy	491
Cylinder head with centre water outlet adaptor for using Aquaplane head with std. cooling system	491/12
Cylinder head stud, long type, for above heads	491/2
Cylinder head chrome dome-nuts	491/3
Cylinder head gasket, solid copper, racing	G/491/c
Cylinder head gasket, C. & A. racing	G/491/H
Cylinder head gasket, standard	G/491/ST
Cylinder head thick washer, for use with alloy heads ...	491/4
Racing camshaft, high lift	600/R
Carburetter, S.U.-Aquaplane, large bore racing	750/10
Carburetter, Zenith downdraft VIG, racing or competition	750/11
Dipstick, for opposite side of sump	612
Distributor, high-speed racing	300
Engine testing for accurate b.h.p. figures	On application
Flywheel, alloy racing, weight 4 lb. 2 oz., with gear ring	1000/R
Flywheel, standard but dynamically balanced	850/ST
Flywheel, lightened and dynamically balanced, otherwise standard	850/BL
Fuel, Aquaplane racing, for comp. r. up to 7 : 1	SRF 10
8 : 1	SRF 20
9 : 1	SRF 30
10 : 1	SRF 40
12 : 1	SRF 50
15 : 1	SRF 60
20 : 1	SRF100

(Note.—Comp. r. figures are given as a guide to fuel only.)

Coil, Lucas sports	635
Manifold, alloy, inlet, type 2VZ, for two std. Ford 10 carburetters or two Zenith VIG carburetters, with cast-in balance pipe	900/2ZB
Manifold, alloy, inlet, type 2VZ, kit ready to fit (less carburetters) with petrol pipe, exhaust cover plate, linkages and choke link wire	900/2ZK
Manifold, alloy, inlet, type 2SU, for two standard bore S.U. carburetters or two special large bore S.U.-Aquaplane carburetters, with cast-in balance pipe ...	900/2SUB
Manifold, alloy, inlet, type 2SU complete with two special large S.U.-Aquaplane carburetters ready to fit	900/2SUK
Manifold, exhaust, racing type, one piece, ejector design	1400
Oil pump, racing high-capacity	700/R
Oil pressure adjuster for high-capacity pump	720/80
Oil pressure gauge, 0/200 lb. per sq. in.	723/200
Tachometer, 0/7,000 r.p.m., 4-in. dial, for use with drive 1500/RC	1501/RC

Tachometer, flexible shaft, length 4 ft. to 7 ft.	1502/RC
Timing case cover, alloy, with built-in tachometer drive ...	1500/RC
Valve chest cover, alloy, ribbed	1100
Valve springs, racing type, up to 7,000 r.p.m.	825/R
Valves lengthened, for racing camshaft	601/R
Water impeller, Ford, for improved cooling	1200/ST
Water impeller, with alloy pulley and body	1200/R

Specialists' recommendations

The information which follows suggests a methodical approach to tuning operations, and has been furnished by Mr. C. D. F. Buckler, whose successes with Buckler Ford Ten Specials are well known. Reference may be made to Chapter 24, Appendix 4, giving some typical performance figures obtained with various items of equipment and degrees of tuning.

First, with regard to the compression ratio; this can be altered in several ways to give different ratios, as follows:—

Comp. r.	How obtained.
6.1 : 1	Std. ratio, std. cyl. head, std. C. & A. gasket.
6.3 : 1	Std. cyl. head, copper gasket, 18 S.W.G.
6.4 : 1	Std. cyl. head, copper gasket, 20 S.W.G.
6.7 : 1	Std. cyl. head, copper gasket, 20 S.W.G., Machine .010 in. from face of head.
7.0 : 1	Std. cyl. head, copper gasket, 20 S.W.G., Machine .025 in. from face of head.
7.2 : 1	Ford 8 cyl. head, std. C. & A. gasket, plus 24 S.W.G. copper gasket.
7.6 : 1	Ford 8 cyl. head, std. C. & A. gasket.
7.8 : 1	Ford 8 cyl. head, copper gasket, 16 S.W.G.
8.2 : 1	Ford 8 cyl. head, copper gasket, 18 S.W.G.
8.5 : 1	Ford 8 cyl. head, copper gasket, 20 S.W.G.

The highest compression ratio mentioned above can be employed with premium fuels, or 50/50 petrol-benzol, providing the vehicle weight does not exceed 10 cwt. For higher comp. r., fuel with an alcohol content is necessary. Copper plating is advantageous on iron heads, in providing improved heat distribution.

When machining the face of the head, make sure that there is plenty of metal left, as heads are apt to vary in this respect as between one casting and another. If possible, and certainly when machining for a high ratio, a head should be used which has a more than average thickness of metal on the face to be machined. Also, it is necessary that both head and block faces should be perfectly flat and clean, but this item is doubly important when thin solid copper gaskets are used instead of the standard C. & A. gasket.

When deciding on a particular compression ratio, full consideration must be given to the fuel to be used, and the ratio suitable for a particular fuel must not be exceeded. Persistent detonation can be very harmful in these engines, leading to trouble with plugs and pistons, and even blown gaskets. If an inferior fuel has unavoidably to be employed for any reason, it will do no harm so long as the throttle opening is kept below that at which pinking occurs, and in fact excellent m.p.g. figures can be obtained in this manner.

For compression ratios higher than those detailed in the foregoing table, a special head is necessary, such as the Aquaplane type already described. Whatever type of head is used, the combustion chambers must be polished and the sharp edges removed. The edge of the head adjacent to the gasket must not be rounded off drastically, but just radiused to eliminate any sharpness. It is a good idea also to remove the inner threads in the spark plug bosses which are not engaged by the plug threads.

Volumetric efficiency

The inlet ports and manifold should be smoothed out and polished as detailed in Chapter 15. It is feasible to fit two carburetters with choke diameter of $1\frac{1}{8}$ in. on inlet pipes of like bore. The inlet ports in this case are opened out to the same diameter at the outer ends and tapered off from thence to the valve throats. Variable choke carburetters (S.U. type) are to be preferred. The valve seats can be enlarged as described in Chapter 15, page 172, to the extent of 1/16 in., still using standard valves. The valves should be radiused off, together with their seats, and the guides dealt with, all as detailed in the aforementioned chapter.

It is considered that r.p.m. in excess of 6,000 should not be attempted, as although higher revolutions can be obtained, bearing loadings are really excessive and the power actually falls off considerably. Double valve springs will take care of valve bounce, but to fit these it is necessary to machine the guides to provide a seating for the inner springs, and also to fit heavy duty retainers. It is considered that genuine Ford valves are superior to others, and therefore no useful purpose is served by experimenting with special valves.

The connecting rods can with advantage be polished all over and checked for alignment, as detailed in Chapter 17, but must not on any account have holes drilled in them for lightening, or have metal removed. Ford standard pistons have proved perfectly adequate for high-speed work, their general design bearing a strong resemblance to racing practice; thus there is little point in experimenting with alternatives. For competing in the 1,100-c.c. class, the block can be linered, and suitable smaller-bore pistons supplied, by firms specializing in such equipment.

Ignition equipment

The standard Ford coil has shown itself capable of providing the required spark intensity at revolutions up to the maximum recommended. Coil ignition is preferable to the use of a magneto, as the latter not only takes power to drive, thus reducing the mechanical efficiency of the engine, but also throws an undesirable load on the drive gears which are naturally designed for the much lighter load of the distributor. A special sports coil may be used if one wishes to experiment, but apart from this, no other coil will give a better performance than the standard one. For high revolutions it is an advantage to duplicate the contact-breaker spring to ensure absolutely positive action. The ignition should not be advanced beyond the recommended standard timing. In fact, when using a raised comp. r., and polished ports, a power gain can usually be obtained by retarding up to 5 deg. from the maker's setting.

When the power output has been considerably increased, it is desirable to strengthen the spring pressure on the clutch, but this must not be overdone or distortion of the toggles will take place.

Sprint racing

For those who are particularly interested in sprint racing, the following information will be of considerable interest. It has been furnished by Mr. O. H. J. Davies, of Castle Garage, Pembroke, himself a sprint enthusiast with much experience in this field of competition work.

In the first place, attention to connecting rod weight on the lines indicated in Chapter 17, page 212, is necessary. The ports should also be dealt with in regard to polishing, and the inlet ports opened out by about $\frac{1}{8}$ in. The valve edges can also be faired off. Reference should be made to pages 172 and 173 of Chapter 15 for details.

Double valve springs are recommended, as are bronze-alloy valve guides. The pistons, of solid-skirt pattern, should be run with .0025 in. greater diametral clearance than standard. The flywheel can also be lightened, or a special lightweight wheel fitted. In machining metal off a standard wheel, it is important not to remove metal from parts subject to stress. The tappet clearance should be .006 in. on inlet and .008 in. on exhaust valves, giving earlier opening and later closing of the valves. This clearance is, of course, much less than standard, and it will be necessary to build up the valve feet and grind off the subsequent surplus metal to arrive at the correct clearance.

The use of a Ford 8 cylinder head will raise the comp. r. to about 8 : 1 with standard gasket. The Davies Special manifolds should be used, comprising an induction manifold carrying two semi-downdraft S.U. carburetters, type H1 for standard port size, and type H2 if the ports have been enlarged. The exhaust manifold is also special, and is of the four-branch type. This should feed to a 2-in. diameter tailpipe running the full length of the car, in conjunction with a silencer of Servais or Burgess pattern. In order to obtain a free flow of cool air to the carburetter intakes, a suitable type of air-scoop must be arranged on the bonnet.

The Ford standard distributor is considered suitable, no advantage having accrued from the use of magneto ignition. In conjunction with the former, a Runbaken Oil-coil, and contact points (platinum) and condenser of the same make are recommended. The contact-breaker gap setting is .010 in.

For comp. r. of about 8 : 1, using the Ford 8 head as described, Champion plugs, type L 10S, or equivalent, will be suitable. Engine oil of SAE 20 viscosity, plus Redex, is used for short sprints, together with Redex only in axle and gear-box. Under these conditions, the following performance has been obtained:—

Maximum r.p.m., 7,000.
Acceleration, 0–50 m.p.h., 7.5 secs.
Max. speed, 88 m.p.h.

The above on a sprint car weighing 9.5 cwt.

The Davies Special manifolds are illustrated on page 179.

CHAPTER 20

Tuning the Jaguar

*The XK120 engine—Fitting special camshafts—Raising the compression ratio—
Other items—The chassis—Special parts list*

The XK120 engine

The information given in this chapter is applicable to the standard XK120 engine, and is based on data supplied by Jaguar Cars Ltd. It will be appreciated that the marketed sports-racing versions of the XK120 incorporate most or all of the special fittings to which reference is made.

The standard engine, designed for operation on pool fuel of about 72 octane rating, has a compression ratio of 7 : 1. On this comp. r. and fuel, however, considerable increase in performance is obtainable by fitting the special inlet and exhaust camshafts, lightened flywheel and crankshaft damper which are available, and using the appropriate types of carburetter needles and spark plugs.

The special camshafts give a .375 in. lift, and can be fitted to engines from No. W4483 onwards without alteration to the head. From engine No. W4012 to W4482 the exhaust valve guides and the inlet and exhaust tappet guides were modified. It is therefore necessary, in order to fit the new camshafts, to reduce the height of the inlet valve guides at the top by 1/16 in. The chamfer at the top of the guide must be retained.

Previous to engine No. W4012, more extensive alterations are necessary. All valve guides (inlet and exhaust) must have their height reduced by 1/16 in., the previous remark regarding chamfer applying. The tappet guide inserts must also be machined to give sufficient clearance for the high-lift cams. The machining involves making a 1/16-in. deep, 45-deg. chamfer at the top of the guide, as indicated on page 233.

Fitting special camshafts

The clearance with the high-lift camshafts is .006 in. inlet and .010 in. exhaust, the valve timing being as standard, and ignition timing 5 deg. before t.d.c. with points just breaking and centrifugal-vacuum control in the static position. The carburetters should be reset with R.F. needles, and Champion L 10S plugs installed. For racing L 11S may be required.

Increased acceleration from lower speeds can be obtained by the use of a lightened flywheel. This must be balanced together with the clutch unit, before fitting. The existing crankshaft damper should be replaced with a special high-r.p.m. damper.

Raising the compression ratio

For use with 80-octane fuel, an 8 : 1 comp. r. is quite acceptable, and in fact engines have formerly been supplied

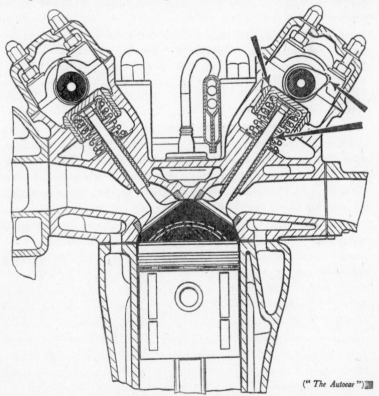

("*The Autocar*")

THE SPECIAL FITTINGS SUPPLIED BY THE MAKERS, AS INDICATED BY THE ARROWS. NOTE ALSO CHAMFER REQUIRED ON VALVE AND TAPPET GUIDES TO CLEAR HIGH-LIFT CAMS

for export only having this ratio, the engine numbers in such cases being followed by the suffix " 8." The valve timing, ignition timing and carburetter needles remain as detailed for the 7 : 1 comp. r. engine, but spark plugs should be Champion NA 8, or NA 10 for racing.

The modified compression ratio is obtained by replacing the existing pistons with ones having higher crowns. The distributor also is replaced by one having a different advance characteristic.

A further compression ratio increase to 9 : 1 is possible, again by the fitting of special pistons. For this ratio, 85-octane fuel is necessary, or 80-octane plus 10 per cent. benzol. In addition to the modifications already specified for the 7 : 1 comp. r. engine, the distributor will again require to be changed, and the timing set to 8 deg. before t.d.c. with automatic advance mechanism in the static position, and points just breaking. The carburetter needles required are type R.B., and spark plugs N12, which are suitable for racing.

Other items

For all three alternative compression ratios, it is advantageous for racing purposes to dispense with the vacuum-operation to the automatic ignition advance. This is done by removing the pipe leading from the carburetter to the vacuum unit and blanking up the hole at the engine end. A less workmanlike method is just to flatten the pipe.

A special dual exhaust system is obtainable which gives increased performance, but reduces the ground clearance by about 2 in. When supplied, a drawing is available showing complete fitting details.

To take care of the increased power output, a special clutch assembly is provided. This, apart from being tested to very high revolutions, has a solid centre plate with the linings riveted and cemented thereto. Maximum friction is thus produced on first engagement for racing starts. A heavy-duty release bearing is included, to withstand the increased spring pressure.

It should be noted that with the modifications carried out, the peak r.p.m. of the engine is increased to about 5,800, as

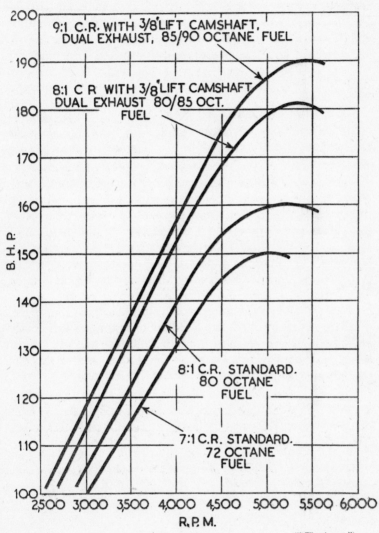

9:1 C.R. WITH 3/8"LIFT CAMSHAFT, DUAL EXHAUST, 85/90 OCTANE FUEL

8:1 C R WITH 3/8"LIFT CAMSHAFT DUAL EXHAUST 80/85 OCT. FUEL

8:1 C.R. STANDARD. 80 OCTANE FUEL

7:1 C.R. STANDARD. 72 OCTANE FUEL

B.H.P.

R.P.M.

("*The Autocar*")

B.H.P./R.P.M. GRAPH OF THE XK120 ENGINE, WITH AND WITHOUT SPECIAL FITTINGS

compared with the 5,200–5,400 of the standard unit. In all cases where the car is used for competition work, the main water thermostat should be removed and its by-pass pipe from the housing blanked off. A manually operated switch, suitably wired to the self-starting carburetter, will enable this to be cut out once the engine has been started from cold.

The Chassis

Both front and rear suspension can be stiffened, and it is recommended that any stiffening is done at both ends of the car, and not just front or rear only. The modification consists of replacing the front torsion bars and the rear springs.

The brakes will give the best results if fitted with Mintex M14 linings, using the standard shoes and drums. For long-distance races, ¼-in. linings in place of the standard 3/16-in. thick ones are recommended, the thicker linings being fitted to special brake shoes. Micro-adjusters for the front brakes (replacing the existing adjusters) and special pull-off springs for all brakes are included with these special shoes. Again, for racing, ventilation should be provided to the rear brakes, by way of holes in the anchor-plates provided with air-scoops on the front or inlet edge. Needless to say, holes should also be provided to the rear of the hub to let the air out. Every effort must be made to get air to the brakes, and to this end, the wheel-spats and nave-plates can be left off.

Several alternative axle ratios are available. The following table gives the speeds on gears, corresponding to an engine speed of 5,800 r.p.m., and using standard road-racing tyres of 600 by 16 in.

Axle ratio.	M.p.h. top gear.	M.p.h. 3rd gear.	M.p.h. 2nd gear.
3.27 : 1	145	106	74
3.64 : 1	139	96	60
3.92 : 1	121	89	—
4.3 : 1	112	81	—

The highest ratio is only suitable for very fast circuits having straights about 3 miles in length. If is, of course, not possible to advise as to which ratio should be used for any particular circuit, as there are far too many factors to be taken into consideration.

Special parts list

The following list summarizes the various parts referred to in the text:—

Item.	Part No.
Exhaust system	C 5700
.375 in. lift camshaft, inlet	C 5717
.375 in. lift camshaft, exhaust	C 5718
Piston, 9 : 1 comp. r.	C 5724
Distributor for 9 : 1 comp. r.	C 5374
Piston, 8 : 1 compr. r.	C 2426
Distributor for 8 : 1 comp. r.	C 2748
Lightened flywheel	C 5808
High r.p.m. crankshaft damper	C 5809
High r.p.m. clutch assy., incl. driven plate and release brg.	C 5722
Driven plate only for above (replacement)	C 5723
1 in. torsion bar, right-hand	C 5719
1 in. torsion bar, left-hand	C 5720
Stiffened rear spring, right-hand	C 5721
Stiffened rear spring, left-hand	C 5721
Set of brake shoes with ½-in. Mintex M14 linings, micro adjusters for front brakes, and pull-off springs for all	C 5725
Bucket seat trimmed Bedford Cord	BD 5893
Racing windscreen and cowling, left-hand drive ...	BD 4470
Racing windscreen and cowling, right-hand drive ...	BD 4471

CHAPTER 21

Tuning the Jowett

*General work—Cylinder heads and ports—Compression ratio—Bearings—
Carburetters—Other engine fittings—Transmission—
Parts available for modifications*

General work

The information in this chapter has been supplied by Jowett Cars Ltd., and applies generally to Javelin engines, most of the suggested modifications being now incorporated as standard in the sports power unit installed in the Jupiter chassis. It is important that, in tackling this work, the general instructions provided in the makers' maintenance manual are adhered to, as naturally quite a lot of dismantling and reassembling tasks of a standard nature will be involved, and these must be carried out in a manner above reproach. With that proviso in mind, the following more specific information can be given.

Cylinder heads and ports

The combustion chambers should be polished all over, and this should also extend to the inlet and exhaust ports, using the methods described in Chapter 15. In addition to this polishing in the case of the exhaust ports, the radius under the lower side of the exhaust valve seating may be considerably increased on earlier models. Later engines have incorporated this alteration, which is made clear in the sketch on page 239. It will be observed that removal of this metal increases the cross-sectional area at the throat of the port.

As regards the inlet ports, early castings have more metal than desirable under the valve seating. On later castings metal has been added to the opposite wall, with improved results. Obviously this cannot be added to earlier types, but the rough edge can be faired off to reduce the buffer effect under the shoulder (see diagram, page 239).

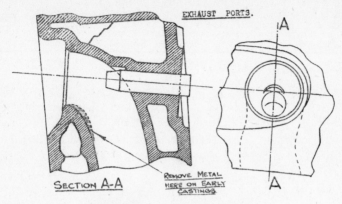

EXHAUST PORTS.

SECTION A-A

REMOVE METAL HERE ON EARLY CASTINGS

MODIFICATION TO EXHAUST PORTS

When polishing the combustion chambers all sharp edges must be removed, and the undercuts round each valve may be blended into the general shape to ensure smooth gas flow and assist turbulence.

The ports and manifolds should be lined up, using the method described in Chapter 15, page 174, and removing metal where necessary to ensure absolutely correct flow-ways.

It is assumed that valves and seats will be in first-class condition, and a seat width of 3/32 in. for exhaust, and 1/16 in. for inlet valve seats must be maintained. Further, it is important that the turbulence angle is maintained in the valve throats below the seating, as shown in the drawing on page 240.

The standard valve springs give r.p.m. of 5,500 without valve-crash intervening. Stronger outer springs can be

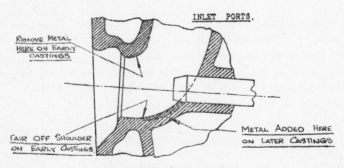

INLET PORTS.

REMOVE METAL HERE ON EARLY CASTINGS

FAIR OFF SHOULDER ON EARLY CASTINGS

METAL ADDED HERE ON LATER CASTINGS

MODIFICATION TO INLET PORTS

fitted (a parts list is given at the end of this section) to increase the valve-crash point.

Compression ratio

After the cylinder heads have been dealt with in accordance with the foregoing, the combustion chamber capacities should be checked by the measurement of liquid volume method described in Chapter 18. The volume should be 40 to 41 c.c. The standard gasket, in compressed form, has

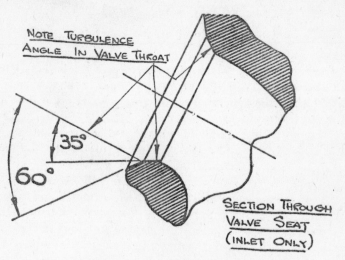

NOTE TURBULENCE ANGLE IN VALVE THROAT

35°

60°

SECTION THROUGH VALVE SEAT (INLET ONLY)

THE TURBULENCE ANGLE IN THE VALVE THROAT MUST BE MAINTAINED, AS SHOWN HERE

a capacity of 7.5 c.c. The above capacities, with standard pistons, give a comp. r. of 7.2 : 1. Higher compression ratios are obtainable, not by machining the head face, but by fitting alternative pistons, which are provided suitable for ratios of 7.6 or 8.0 : 1. These pistons should, of course, only be used with premium fuels of at least 80-octane rating.

A final check on compression ratio can be made with the cylinder heads in position. After ensuring that both valves are closed on the cylinder which is being checked, get the piston at t.d.c. and fill the chamber with light oil from a burette until the level is flush with the spark plug aperture but not coming up the threads. It is important to ensure that all air is ejected, and gentle rocking of the engine shaft (taking care not to open a valve) will ensure this. For the three compression ratios, the volumes injected should be as follows:—

Comp. r. 7.2 : 1	Volume 58 c.c.
„ 7.6 : 1	„ 56 „
„ 8.0 : 1	„ 53 „

An error of plus 2 per cent. is allowable in the above volumes, but if any correction in capacity is required as between cylinder heads it is permissible to machine a small amount off the head face. Reducing this by .011 in. reduces the capacity by 1 c.c.

Bearings

Engines up to No. EO/PB/8902 were fitted with white-metal main and big-end bearings and an unhardened crank-shaft. It is advisable to replace this assembly with an induction-hardened shaft, using copper-lead bearings (except the rear main, which remains of white metal). In carrying out this modification it is essential to adhere to precision practice in regard to cleanliness, and also to take great care in remaking the seal of the balance-pipe rubber ring as detailed on page 35 of the Jowett *Maintenance Manual*.

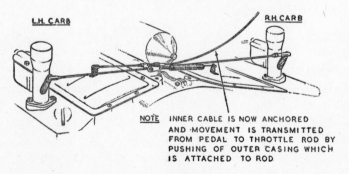

NOTE INNER CABLE IS NOW ANCHORED AND MOVEMENT IS TRANSMITTED FROM PEDAL TO THROTTLE ROD BY PUSHING OF OUTER CASING WHICH IS ATTACHED TO ROD

REARRANGEMENT OF THROTTLE-OPERATING CABLE FOR USE WITH SPECIAL CARBURETTERS

R

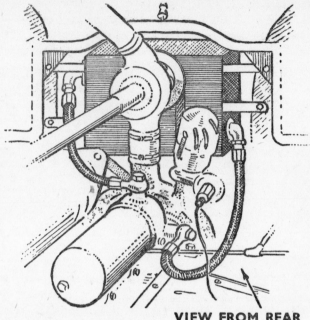

VIEW FROM REAR

ARRANGEMENT OF OIL-FILTER INCORPORATING COOLER ASSEMBLY

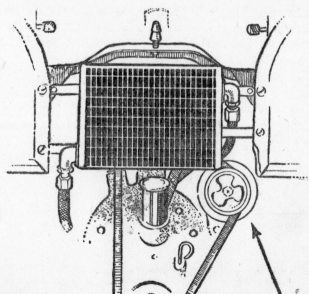

FRONT VIEW OF COOLER (GRILLE REMOVED)

ARRANGEMENT OF OIL-FILTER INCORPORATING COOLER ASSEMBLY

Carburetters

Special carburetters, type 30VM, should be used, with the following settings: 27-mm. choke, 110 main, 50 compensating, 2.2 vent over capacity, 45 slow-running, 120 progression.

A 1.5-mm. needle seating (1-mm. washer) should be used in place of the standard VM4 or 5. The throttle spindle operation is in the reverse direction to standard, and in consequence it is necessary to rearrange the throttle-operating cable. A good method is to fit a cable about 9 in. longer than standard, securing the inner cable to the bracket on the left-hand tappet cover, and the outer casing to the throttle rod. The throttle return spring should then be connected to the clip to which the original outer cable was secured on the right-hand tappet cover. The diagram, page 241, will make the layout clear.

Other engine fittings

On all engines prior to No. PA5857, it is advisable to modify the water pump to increase its capacity to 7 galls. per min. at 1,500 r.p.m. This alteration was incorporated in later engines, and consists of a redesigned cover and the addition of a shroud assembly to the impeller.

Again, on engines prior to the above number, the two bleed holes in the thermostat should be enlarged to a diameter of 3/16 in.

An oil-pump of increased capacity was fitted to engines subsequent to PA800, and it is recommended that this be fitted to earlier engines which are being modified for extra performance.

The rear timing case cover and early type oil filter assembly fitted on engines up to EI/PC/16603, should be replaced by the latest type assembly which allows an oil cooler to be incorporated, the cooler connections being by flexible piping, as shown on page 242.

The fan blades should be made more rigid by extra welding along the base of the blade where it abuts on to the centre spider. This will call for rebalancing the fan assembly, which can be done by mounting it on a suitable mandrel and rolling along knife edges. If it is required to remove metal for balancing, this can be taken off the tips of the blades affected.

The recommended ignition setting is with the points just breaking at about .025 in. after t.d.c. measured on the flywheel rim. This will cause pinking at about one-third to one-half throttle at 20–30 m.p.h., when the vacuum-operated advance mechanism is operating. The pinking should disappear at full throttle.

Transmission

It is desirable to replace the clutch driven plate with one having a woven lining with a greater coefficient of friction, as detailed in the parts list given later on.

Special constant-mesh gears providing a higher ratio in the intermediates are available, the chart, below, showing the road characteristics. These ratios are incorporated in cars with gearboxes numbered 31 and upwards on the box top.

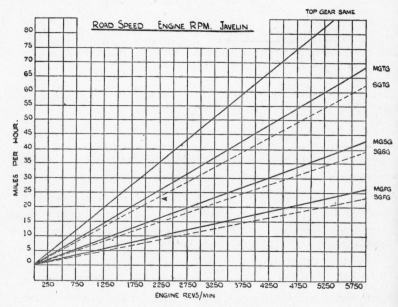

GRAPH OF M.P.H./R.P.M. JOWETT JAVELIN ENGINE

The propeller shaft universal joints, particularly at the front, should have a careful examination, particularly after about 6,000 miles and if any of the rubbers show signs of cracking around the studs, the joint should be replaced. High-duty brake linings, Mintex M14 or 15, or Ferodo MR41, should be used for high-speed competition work. When ordering it is necessary to specify whether the car has the early hydraulic front and mechanical rear system, or the later fully hydraulic operation.

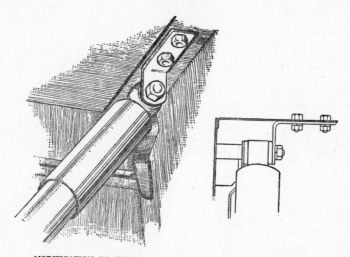

MODIFICATION TO UPPER PIVOT-PIN OF REAR SHOCK-ABSORBER

A modification to the rear shock-absorber was introduced at car No. 17672, this consisting of stiffening-up the upper pin. It is advisable to check that this has been done on the particular car. If not, the pin mounting can be modified as shown in the diagram.

A 25 per cent. stiffer all-round shock-absorber setting is recommended for most types of competition work. Since an alteration in the setting involves dismantling of all the shock-absorbers, it is just as well to replace them by a stronger type.

The batteries are rather exposed at the bottom and front, for high-speed work over loose going, and a sheet-metal cover should be arranged to protect them.

Parts available for modifications

The following list covering the parts referred to is included for ready reference:—

Item.	Part No.
Stronger outer valve spring	52964
Piston, comp. r. 7.6 : 1	53228
Piston, comp. r. 8.0 : 1	53227
Induction-hardened crankshaft	50647
Copper-lead connecting rod brg. assy.	J 54444
Copper-lead main brgs., front and centre	52573
White-metal rear main brg.	50646
Higher-coefficient clutch driven plate	52426/A
30VM carburetter, left-hand	I. 53732
30VM carburetter, right-hand	I. 53733
New type water pump cover	52710
New type water pump impeller	J 54414
Latest type thermostat	50768
Increased capacity oil pump	A.S. 52403
Latest type rear timing case cover	53030
Tecalemit oil filter assy.	53422
Oil cooler	J 54532
Flexible pipes to oil cooler (2)	J 54519
Higher ratio stem gear (gearbox)	52733
Higher ratio layshaft (gearbox)	52734
Stiffer shock-absorbers, front	54385
Stiffer shock-absorbers, rear	50467 S

Road characteristics

Rear axle ratio 4.875 : 1. Rolling radius of tyre, size 5.25 by 16 in.—12.7 in.

Gear ratio.	Standard box.	Modified box.
Bottom	1 : 19	1 : 17.4
Second	1 : 11.6	1 : 10.6
Third	1 : 7.34	1 : 6.7
Top	1 : 4.875	1 : 4.875

CHAPTER 22

Tuning the M.G.

The standard engine—Tuning in five stages—Genera lobservations

The standard engine

The M.G. Car Company Ltd. may justifiably claim to have originated the system of tuning by "stages." The Company are also in a position to supply the special components required for the modifications, which enable a power output of nearly 100 b.h.p. to be obtained without alteration to the main components, i.e., crankshaft, connecting rods, etc.

Before giving details of the five tuning stages, it will be useful to tabulate the data of the standard engine as a basis for comparison. The details refer to the TD type engine, but TB and TC units are exactly the same except for very minor items which do not affect the information.

Apart from the general information given in Chapter 14, the following should also be noted:—

Carburetter bore: 1.25 in.
Carburetter jet: .090
Carburetter needles: Standard, ES; Richer, DK; Weaker, EF.
Safe max. r.p.m.: 5,700.
Valve-crash r.p.m.: 6,000.
Capacity of combustion space: 45.5 c.c.
Cylinder head depth, top to bottom faces: 76.75 mm.
Gasket thickness: .045 in.
Gasket volume (in position): 4.5 c.c.

Tuning in five stages

Stage 1 tuning

This stage of power increase involves largely the treatment of the combustion chambers, ports and manifold flanges as

detailed in Chapter 15.   In addition, the comp. r. is raised
to 8.6 : 1 by machining 3/32 in. from the face of the head.
The head thickness after machining (top to bottom faces) will
then be 74.37 mm.   The standard gasket is retained, care
being taken that its edge is clear of the combustion chamber.
This should be watched at the point where the plug aperture
meets the face, as it will probably be necessary to file back a
sharp edge at this point.   The edge should be not less than
1/32 in. thick, and should be radiused nicely into the shape
of the combustion chamber.   Although there should be
plenty of machined face for the protection of the gasket after
this operation, there is no point in filing back too far.

The reduced depth of head will necessitate the use of
packing pieces under the rocker standards, and these should
be 1/16 in. thick, of mild steel, holes being drilled as necessary
to match the bases of the standards.   3/32 in. thick washers
will also be required on the cylinder head studs under the
holding-down nuts.

When polishing the inlet ports, do not alter the shape
internally.   The separating boss between the siamesed ports
may be filed and streamlined in the direction of gas flow, so
that oblong ports are obtained with a height of 1 3/16 in. and
a width of 11/16 in.   The boss must on no account be removed
altogether, as it has an important effect on the distribution
of mixture between the ports.

For reduction of valve gear friction (and thus an increase
in mechanical efficiency), the spacing springs on the rocker
shaft should be replaced by tubing, as detailed in Chapter 16,
page 199.   The tubing should preferably be phosphor-bronze,
but mild-steel will serve.   The end-float on the rockers
must not exceed .003 in.

The 8.6 : 1 comp. r. is very suitable for use with premium
brand fuels, and for fast touring the author has found the
standard Champion L 10S plugs perfectly adequate.   However, for sustained high speeds, it may be necessary to use a
slightly hotter plug such as Champion LA 11 or Lodge R 49.

The power output for Stage 1 is approximately 58 b.h.p.
at 5,000 r.p.m., and 60 at 5,500 to 6,000 r.p.m.

Performance curves for all stages of tuning are shown on
page 249.

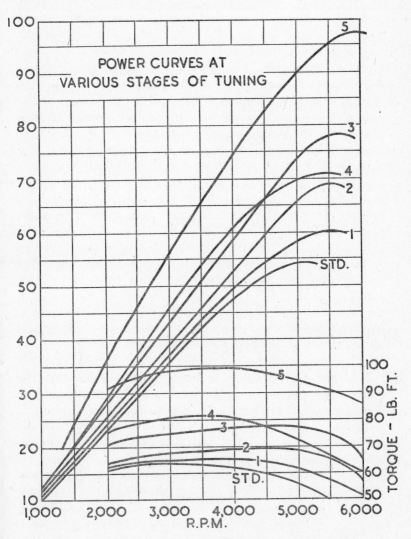

POWER CURVES OF M.G. ENGINES, TYPE TB, TC, AND TD, WITH VARIOUS
STAGES OF TUNING

Stage 2 tuning

This stage involves another increase in compression ratio, plus the fitting of larger valves and stronger valve springs, with ports modified to take the valves. The replacement springs allow of 6,000 r.p.m. without valve-crash.

The compression ratio is raised to 9.3 : 1 by machining $\frac{1}{8}$ in. from the head face, the depth from top to bottom faces after machining then being 73.575 mm. This is the absolute maximum that may be removed, any further comp. r. increase being obtained by the use of special pistons.

The effect (of machining the head) on the spark plug recess, will be even more marked than in the case of Stage 1, and this must be watched. To fit the larger inlet valves, which have 36-mm. heads, part of the combustion chamber wall must be cut away to clear the head. This can be done with a 38-mm. diameter side-and-face cutter, using the valve guide as a pilot. The cutter corner should have a 1-mm. radius. Alternatively to the use of a cutter, the combustion chamber can be ground carefully, until the valve head has 1 mm. working clearance. The valve port below the valve is similarly increased to 33-mm. diameter, and the seat recut to 34.9 mm. top diameter, with an angle of 30 deg. Any ridges left by these operations should be smoothed off.

The exhaust valve ports require similar treatment to allow the 34-mm. headed valves to be installed. In this case, the cutter is 36-mm. diameter, the valve port below valve 29-mm. diameter, and the valve seat 32.8 mm. with 30-deg. angle.

The stronger valve springs are interchangeable with the standard springs, but have staggered pitch, the closed coils going next to the cylinder head. The loading is 150 lb. open, and valve-crash occurs at about 6,500 r.p.m. The rocker-shaft standards require packing-up as for Stage 1. $\frac{1}{8}$-in. thick washers are necessary on the head studs. Using plugs, carburetter, rocker and ignition settings as for Stage 1, with fuel 75 per cent. benzol and 25 per cent. petrol, the following output should be available:—

$$61 \text{ b.h.p. at } 5,000 \text{ r.p.m.}$$
$$65 \quad ,, \quad 5,500 \quad ,,$$
$$63 \quad ,, \quad 6,000 \quad ,,$$

With carburetter needles RO in jets .090 in., and using fuel of 50 per cent. methanol, 20 per cent. petrol and 30 per cent. benzol, power should be as follows:—

> 62.5 b.h.p. at 5,000 r.p.m.
> 66.5   ,,   5,500   ,,
> 64   ,,   6,000   ,,

Where a methanol fuel is used, 1 per cent. (approximately) castor oil should be added. Carburetter needles alternative to those specified are—richer, RLS, or weaker, No. 5. Quite a lot of fuel is required to flow at times, and twin S.U. pumps are desirable, using a fuel line from each of the pumps to a carburetter, with an interconnecting pipe between the two carburetters. This will need a double-feed banjo union to be fitted on each float-chamber.

In place of the standard carburetters, 1½-in. instruments can be fitted, with needles EL in jets .090 in. Using fuel comprising 75 per cent. benzol and 25 per cent. petrol, the following output should be obtained:—

> 63 b.h.p. at 5,000 r.p.m.
> 68 ,,   5,500   ,,
> 66 ,,   6,000   ,,

Alternative carburetter needles are—richer, AA, or weaker, EO. With carburetter needles RLS in jets .090 in., and with fuel of 50 per cent. methanol, 20 per cent. petrol and 30 per cent. benzol, the following should be the output:—

> 66 b.h.p. at 5,000 r.p.m.
> 70 ,,   5,500   ,,
> 68 ,,   6,000   ,,

Alternative carburetter needles for the above fuel are—richer, CS2, or weaker, RO. If richer needles are fitted, change to the .100 in. jet range.

Stage 3 tuning

This stage of super-tuning provides the highest output obtainable with atmospheric induction. A compression ratio of 12 to 1 is used, this involving the fitting of special pistons. The cylinder head remains unaltered from standard, with a depth of 76.75 mm., and the standard gasket is used. No packing pieces are therefore required on the rocker-shaft standards.

The pistons have flame grooves therein, and must be fitted so that these are on the spark plug side. For this high compression ratio, very particular attention has to be given to the fuel, which is as follows : 80 per cent. dry blending methanol, with specific gravity of .796 at 60 deg. F.; 10 per cent. benzol (90), specific gravity .8758 at 60 deg. F.; 10 per cent. petrol, 70 or 80 octane; 1 per cent. castor oil.

The standard carburetters can be used, with jets .100 in. and needles GK. Richer needles are RC, and weaker, RV. The float-chamber needles and seatings must be S.U. type T.3, to suit the increased fuel flow. Champion plugs LA 14 or Lodge R 49 will be suitable, and the ignition setting should be altered to 4 deg. after t.d.c., for initial try-out. Duplicate fuel pumps will be necessary, arranged as detailed for Stage 2.

The rockers should be set at .022 in. clearance.

With the above alterations, the output available should be:

$$
\begin{array}{lll}
69 \text{ b.h.p. at} & 5,000 & \text{r.p.m.} \\
73 \quad ,, & 5,500 & ,, \\
74 \quad ,, & 5,800 & ,, \\
73 \quad ,, & 6,000 & ,,
\end{array}
$$

If larger valves and stronger springs are fitted, as for Stage 2, the maximum power will be increased to 76 b.h.p. at 5,800 r.p.m.

A further increase is obtainable by fitting the 1½-in. carburetters, to which reference was made in dealing with Stage 2. When mounting these, the manifold entrance ports should be enlarged to 1½ in. to match the carburetter outlets. The increased diameter of 1½ in. cannot be taken right through, but must be tapered off to 1⅜ in. in a length of about ¾ in. of pipe. This minimum of 1⅜ in., representing an area of 1.5 sq. in., should be maintained right through.

The carburetters should have .125-in. jets with VE needles. Richer needle is VG, weaker, VA. The return springs above the light aluminium carburetter pistons can be removed if maximum power is required, but for acceleration and general efficient running, they are better left in position.

Assuming the use of the large valves, fuel, etc., as already detailed for Stage 2, the maximum power will be 80 b.h.p. at 6,000 r.p.m. If a fuel mixture of 100 per cent. methanol is used, with VJ needles in the .125-in. jets (richer VL, weaker V1) 83 b.h.p. will be developed at the same revolutions.

Stage 4 tuning

This stage covers the use of a supercharger of the type described in Chapter 24, fitted to the standard engine. Taking the Shorrock equipment as typical, with a maximum boost of 6 lb. per sq. in. at 5,000 r.p.m., this is fitted with $1\frac{3}{8}$-in. carburetter with jet .090 in. and needle RLS. Fuel is petrol of 70 octane rating. Spark plugs should be Champion L 11S or Lodge HNP, and the rocker clearance is set at .022 in. The following output should be obtained:—

> 45 b.h.p. at 3,000 r.p.m.
> 58   ,,   4,000   ,,
> 69   ,,   5,000   ,,
> 69   ,,   5,500   ,,

If 90 octane fuel can be obtained another 1 b.h.p. will be added to the above figures at the upper end of the r.p.m. scale.

With a fuel mixture comprising 50 per cent. methanol, 20 per cent. petrol, and 30 per cent. benzol, the carburetter will need modifications comprising .125-in. jet and VE needle (richer, VG, weaker, VA), T3 float needle and seating in the float chamber, and twin pumps. Plugs should be Champion L 11S or Lodge HNP. If harder plugs are found necessary, try Champion LA 11 or Lodge R 49. With these modifications, the following power should be developed:—

> 52   b.h.p. at 3,000 r.p.m.
> 68.5   ,,   4,000   ,,
> 75   ,,   5,000   ,,
> 75.5   ,,   5,500   ,,
> 75   ,,   6,000   ,,

Stage 5 tuning

This, the final stage, incorporates many of the Stage 2 alterations, plus the use of a blower as Stage 4. The compression ratio is raised to 9.3 to 1, and large inlet and exhaust valves are installed, plus stronger springs, all as detailed for Stage 2. The carburetter is fitted with VG needle in the .125-in. jet, the richer needle being VI, and weaker VE. All these needles have ⅛-in. shanks.

Twin fuel pumps will, of course, be required, and suitable plugs are Champion LA 11 or LA 14, or Lodge R 49 or R 51. Using a fuel mixture comprising 50 per cent. methanol, 20 per cent. petrol, and 30 per cent. benzol, plus 1 per cent. castor oil, the following performance should be obtained:—

55.5	b.h.p. at	3,000	r.p.m.
73.5	,,	4,000	,,
85.5	,,	5,000	,,
88	,,	5,500	,,
88	,,	6,000	,,

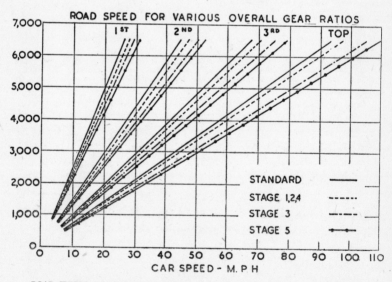

ROAD SPEEDS AT VARIOUS STAGES OF TUNING THE TD TYPE M.G., WITH GEAR RATIOS AS FOLLOWS: STANDARD 5.125:1, 14.42 M.P.H. PER 1,000 R.P.M.; STAGES 1, 2 AND 4, 4.875:1, 15.195 M.P.H. PER 1,000 R.P.M.; STAGE 3, 4.55:1, 16.25 M.P.H. PER 1,000 R.P.M.; STAGE 5, 4.55:1, 17 M.P.H. PER 1,000 R.P.M. (6-IN. TYRES)

A further increase can be obtained by fitting a carburetter of 1¾ in. diameter, this being S.U. type H 6, Spec. No. 538. This must be fitted to a special elbow to match up with the blower inlet, the inside diameter of the pipe being 1¾ in. The jet diameter is .1875 in., with needle RM 7 (richer RM 8, weaker RM 6).

With a fuel of 80 per cent. methanol, 10 per cent. petrol, and 10 per cent. benzol, the following figures should be available:—

$$
\begin{array}{lll}
74.5 \text{ b.h.p. at} & 4,000 & \text{r.p.m.} \\
82 \quad ,, & 4,500 & ,, \\
89 \quad ,, & 5,000 & ,, \\
94.25 \quad ,, & 5,500 & ,, \\
97.5 \quad ,, & 6,000 & ,,
\end{array}
$$

General observations

It is a good idea to add a small percentage of castor oil whenever methanol is used in the fuel. An additional 1 b.h.p. is also available at maximum revs if the fan blades are removed, this representing the power absorbed by this component. Cooling without the fan is adequate providing the speed can be kept above about 40 m.p.h.

The increase in rocker clearance to .022 in. will lead to quite a lot of extra noise from the valve gear. If this is objected to, the standard clearance of .019 in. can be retained, but a loss of about 1 b.h.p. must be accepted.

A considerable reduction in valve-gear noise, even with the larger clearance, can be effected by fitting an aluminium alloy rocker-cover, a type designed by the author being illustrated on page 184. Such a fitting also enables an absolutely oil-tight joint to be obtained, a matter of some difficulty on the standard fitting.

The following schedule of material is given for easy reference, the parts being obtainable from the M.G. Car Company Ltd., or as detailed.

Item.	Part No.
Rocker shaft packing pieces, 1/16 in. thick ...	MG 862/459
36 mm. inlet valve	MG 862/460
34 mm. exhaust valve	MG 862/461
Piston, 12 : 1 comp. r. with rings and pin ...	MG 862/458
Valve spring, outer, 150 lb.	MG 862/462
Valve spring, inner, 150 lb.	MG 862/463
S.U. carburetter, two off, 1.5 in. dia., Spec.	
532	Refer to makers
.100 jets, S.U., No. 1394-112/L	,, ,,
.125 jets, S.U., No. 4185	,, ,,
.1875 jets, fixed type	,, ,,

Jet needles, as S.U. list, obtainable from makers.

Float chamber seat and needle assemblies, S.U., No. T 3 (these are identifiable by three grooves machined around body).

1.75 in. carburetter for use with blower, S.U., Spec. 538.

Plugs—Champion

L 11S	Super sports.
LA 11	Racing 1st step.
LA 14	Racing 2nd step.
LA 15	Racing 3rd step.

Plugs—Lodge

HNP	Super sports.
R 49	Racing 1st step.
R 51	Racing 2nd step.
R 53	Racing 3rd step.

Lucas high-performance coil, type BR 12, for r.p.m. up to 8,000. Standard coil is satisfactory up to 6,000 r.p.m.

Lucas 4 VRA vertical magneto. Lucas Part No. ENM 2002. This has a suitable advance curve for the M.G. engine. To fit, it is necessary to indent push-rod cover plate and move breather pipe elbow.

CHAPTER 23

Miscellaneous Engine Tuning

The A.C.—Ford o.h.v. engines—The s.v. Morris Minor—Sunbeam-Talbot

The A.C.

The well-tried 2-litre A.C. engine, an excellent example of single-o.h.c. design, has not been seen in competition work to a very great extent. Nevertheless, there are many enthusiastic owners who will be interested to know the possibilities in the way of increasing the power output.

The engine develops in standard form, 74 b.h.p. at 4,500 r.p.m. on a comp. r. of 6.5 : 1. It is not feasible to machine the cylinder head to increase the compression ratio, but special pistons can be supplied by the makers giving ratios of 6.75 or 7 : 1. The former, used with fuel of about 72 octane rating, will increase the b.h.p. to 76, while the latter, for which 80–82 octane fuel is necessary, will give an increase to 82 b.h.p. It is not recommended that a higher comp. r. than 7.5 : 1 be employed.

In addition to the fitting of special pistons, the attention to ports, etc., as detailed in Chapter 15 is well worth while. The standard carburetters, which have a bore of 1.125 in., can be replaced with larger ones, bore 1.25 in., a replacement manifold being necessary to take these. The standard rocker clearance of .020 in. can also be increased to .025 in., with some advantage at high revolutions. The valve-gear will, of course, be somewhat noisier.

Ford o.h.v. engines

The o.h.v. Ford engines are now receiving attention from several concerns. On pages 177 and 178 we illustrate an interesting conversion made by Mr. V. A. Fox, of Central Garage, Bangor, for a Consul engine. While at the time of writing, performance figures are not available, there is little doubt that a considerable increase in power output will be obtained.

It will be seen that the modification comprises the use of a four-branch exhaust manifold and the fitting of separate intake pipes for two downdraft carburetters. Quite a lot of machining work was necessary on the head exterior to accommodate the new flange-fitting attachments for the manifolds.

Another interesting conversion is offered by Raymond Mays and Partners Ltd., of Bourne, for the Zephyr engine. This comprises a triple-carburetter induction layout, port modifications, polishing of ports and combustion chambers, and machining of the head face to raise the comp. r. to 7.6 : 1. The normal valve springs are retained, but supplemented by additional inner springs. A Servais silencer is also fitted.

The three carburetters are S.U. type H 4, each one being flange-mounted to the siamesed inlet ports. The three intakes are coupled by a small-diameter balance-pipe. No alteration is made to the standard exhaust manifold.

Some impressive performance figures have been recorded in a car modified as above, the acceleration time through the gears from 0-60 m.p.h. being cut by nearly 4 seconds.

An illustration of the Raymond Mays modified cylinder head is shown on page 187.

The s.v. Morris Minor

Modifications to this well-made side-valve unit generally take the form of the fitting of twin-carburetter induction systems, or low-pressure supercharging. Specialists in both fields are listed in Appendix 3. For those interested in a worth-while increase in performance with premium fuel, with or without further refinements, it may be stated that machining .030 in. from the cylinder head face will increase the comp. r. from the standard 6.5 : 1 to 7.2 : 1. (See also page 187)

Sunbeam-Talbot

A tuning-in-stages sequence for these cars has been initiated by those well-known exponents of the make—George

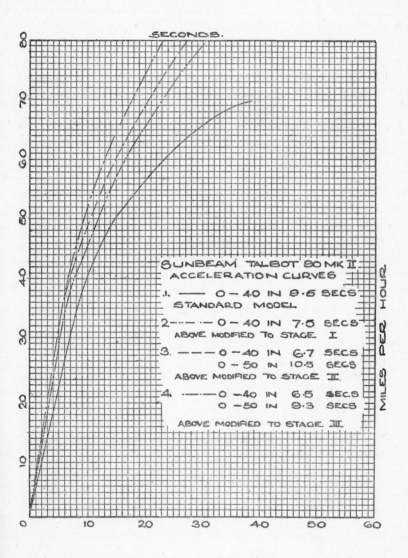

SECONDS.

SUNBEAM TALBOT 90 MK II
ACCELERATION CURVES

1. —— 0 – 40 IN 9·5 SECS
STANDARD MODEL

2. —·—·— 0 – 40 IN 7·5 SECS
ABOVE MODIFIED TO STAGE I

3. ———— 0 – 40 IN 6·7 SECS
          0 – 50 IN 10·5 SECS
ABOVE MODIFIED TO STAGE II.

4. —·—·— 0 – 40 IN 6·5 SECS
          0 – 50 IN 9·3 SECS

ABOVE MODIFIED TO STAGE III

MILES PER HOUR

Hartwell Ltd., of Bournemouth. The standard Sunbeam-Talbot 90 engine develops 70 b.h.p. at 4,000 r.p.m., on a comp. r. of 6.45 : 1. The Hartwell tuning stages involve the following:—

Stage 1

Approximately 77 b.h.p. at 4,500 r.p.m. is available. The cylinder head is modified by attention to valve ports and combustion chambers. The comp. r. is raised to 7.24 : 1 by machining the cylinder head face. A larger carburetter choke is fitted, with altered inlet manifold and partial elimination of hot-spot for greater volumetric efficiency.

Stage 2

This produces about 80 b.h.p. at 4,700 r.p.m. The ports and combustion chambers receive attention as for Stage 1, but the comp. r. is raised to 7.5 : 1. The flywheel is lightened and balanced in a unit with the clutch and crankshaft, while specially graded pistons are fitted, and the connecting rods polished all over. The internal water trough in the head is modified to give increased flow to the vicinity of the exhaust valves.

Stage 3

This stage is similar to Stage 2, but in addition, special aluminium induction manifolds are used, carrying two down-draft carburetters. This results in a power increase to 84 b.h.p. at 4,800 r.p.m.

Performance curves for the above stages of tuning are shown on page 259.

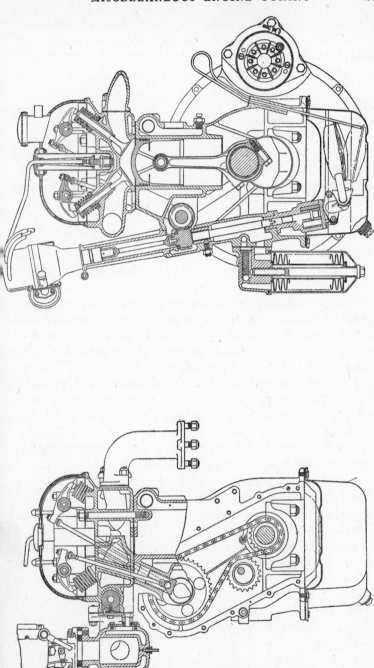

ALL THE MAKINGS OF A SPORTS UNIT, THE ARMSTRONG-SIDDELEY SAPPHIRE, OF 3,435 C.C. 150 B.H.P. AT 5,000 R.P.M., AT PRESENT POWERING A LUXURY SALOON

("*Motor Trader*")

CHAPTER 24

Rational Supercharging

*Objects of forced induction—Supercharger design—Comparison of types—
Performance of blown engines*

Objects of forced induction

The function of a supercharger is to enable a greater weight
of mixture to be supplied to the engine than can be induced
by atmospheric pressure. Very roughly, a 1,500 c.c.
capacity engine supercharged to 5 lb. per sq. in. above
atmospheric, will have the same effective cubic capacity as an
unblown 2-litre unit, since it receives its mixture at 20 lb.
per sq. in. instead of 15.

When considering supercharging as a means of increasing
power output from a given capacity of engine, there are two
general aspects to be dealt with. First, it will be realized that
with the induction system under pressure, torque can readily
be maintained as speed increases, since the blower is able to
pump the mixture through the obstructions caused by rapid
valve operation and thus to fill the cylinders. In this way,
the blower can be used to prolong the power curve in the right
direction to a higher maximum r.p.m. than standard, but this
calls for a very large factor of safety in the reciprocating parts
and crankshaft if trouble is to be avoided.

The alternative, and one which has been popularized to
a considerable degree by makers who have marketed supercharger installations readily adaptable to fit well-known makes
of engine, is to use a low-pressure blower to increase the
torque throughout the range of r.p.m., thus giving a marked
increase in power without going above the designed maximum
revolutions of the engine to more than a very small extent. In
this case, there will be no more increase in inertia stresses than
would be obtained on a tuned " atmospheric " engine, while
the torque increase would probably enable higher gear ratios
to be used.

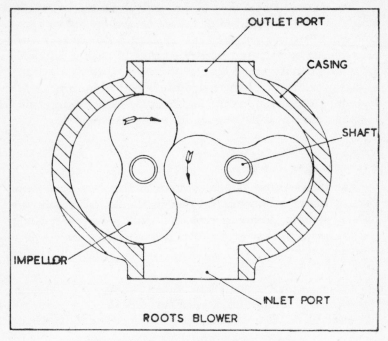

OUTLET PORT

CASING

SHAFT

IMPELLOR

INLET PORT

ROOTS BLOWER

DIAGRAMMATIC LAYOUT OF ROOTS-TYPE BLOWER

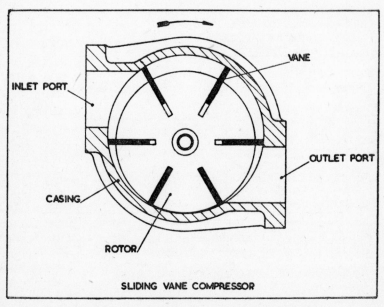

VANE

INLET PORT

OUTLET PORT

CASING

ROTOR

SLIDING VANE COMPRESSOR

DIAGRAMMATIC LAYOUT OF SLIDING VANE COMPRESSOR

The increased heat flow as the result of burning a greater weight of mixture in the same space has obviously to be taken care of, but the great majority of engines to which super-chargers are added are perfectly capable of dealing with this extra heat without modification to valves or cooling system, always providing the blower pressure is kept within reasonable bounds. A rational pressure for the normal sports-type engine is approximately 6 lb. per sq. in. above atmospheric.

Supercharger design

The blower takes power to drive, but in considering this point it must be remembered that in the normal engine the pistons perform pumping work in inhaling the charge, and

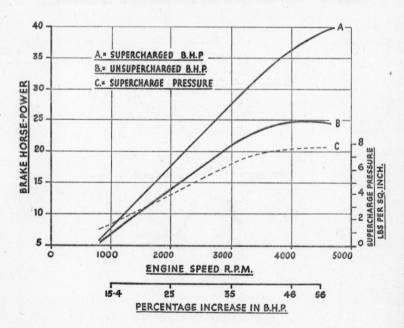

SERIES M.M. MORRIS MINOR ENGINE:
COMPARATIVE PERFORMANCE CURVES
WHEN FITTED WITH A STANDARD SHORROCK SUPERCHARGER TYPE A75.

A.= SUPERCHARGED B.H.P
B.= UNSUPERCHARGED B.H.P.
C.= SUPERCHARGE PRESSURE

that this work is removed from them and transferred to the blower when the latter is installed. Thus, in general, the power absorbed in driving the blower amounts to that required to overcome frictional losses, and therefore the efficiency of the blower as a pump, and the power loss in its rotor and drive, have an important bearing on the overall engine efficiency. *Vis-a-vis* the increase in torque, the supercharged engine should not show inferior consumption figures in comparison with an unblown engine of equal performance.

There are several makes of proprietary supercharger now obtainable, and details of the manufacturers will be found in Appendix 3. There are two main types, these being the geared rotor or Roots blower, and the eccentric-drum vane type.

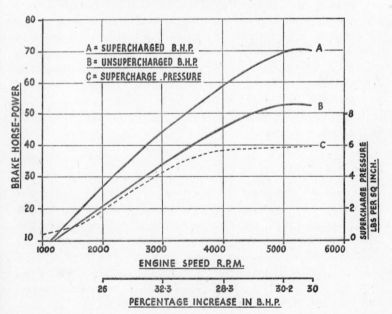

1250 c.c. M.G. ENGINE
TYPE. XPAG
COMPARATIVE PERFORMANCE CURVES
WHEN FITTED WITH A STANDARD SHORROCK SUPERCHARGER TYPE A75.

Reference to the diagrams on page 263 will show the layouts of the two types. In the case of the Roots blower, the two rotors are synchronized by external gearing, and run at an extremely fine clearance between themselves and the casing. The mixture is carried round between the rotors and the outer casing, from intake to delivery port.

With two-lobe rotors as shown, the pumping action has a definite cyclic variation of volume which is dependent on the speed of operation. A steady delivery can be obtained by the use of three-lobe rotors, in conjunction with skewed intake and delivery ports, but these features do not affect the principle of operation.

In the vane-type blower, the rotor and casing are so disposed by reason of their eccentricity to each other, as to form a crescent-shaped chamber with circular end-plates. The four vanes, passing through the rotor and having very fine clearances between their extremities and the casing and end-plates, virtually sub-divide the crescent-shaped chamber into four separate portions. The intake port on the casing is positioned so that as one of the portions receives its full volume of mixture, the adjacent portion, on the intake side of the unit, is increasing in volume and creating a vacuum at the intake port. As soon as the vanes have reached a position where the portion of the chamber between them contains its maximum volume, the volume between the vanes begins to diminish, since the space between the rotor and casing becomes progressively less as the delivery port is approached. Thus, the mixture is compressed inside the casing before it is released to the delivery port.

Comparison of types

It will be seen from the foregoing that in the case of the Roots blower there is no change of total volume throughout the pumping cycle, and thus no internal compression. The mixture, after inhalation, is expelled from the delivery port against the back-pressure in the inlet manifold. The type has the important advantage of requiring no lubricant to the pumping chamber, as there is no running contact therein. The synchronizing gears are carried externally in their own

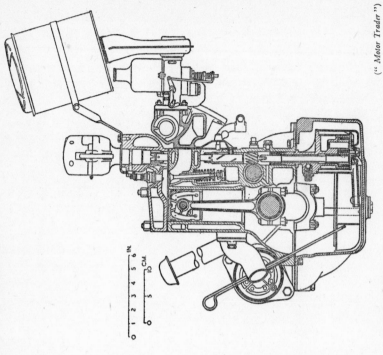

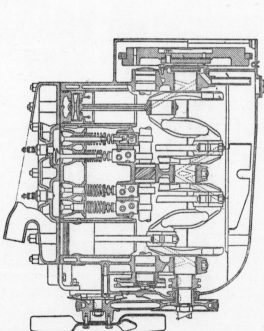

("Motor Trader")

THE SIDE-VALVE MORRIS MINOR—AN INEXPENSIVE UNIT RESPONSIVE TO TUNING OPERATIONS

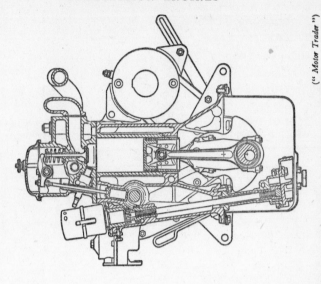

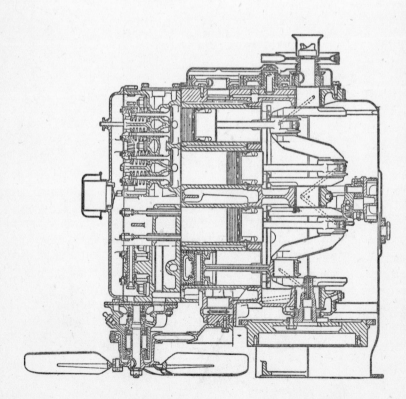

CONTINENTAL PRACTICE FOR COMPARISON—THE EFFICIENT 750-C.C. RENAULT UNIT. NOTE THE VERY HIGH CAMSHAFT

(" *Motor Trader* ")

self-lubricating housing, and frictional losses are small in well-made examples.

The vane-type blower is a true compressor, and thus takes advantage of the laws governing compression. As an example of this, it will be evident that as the compression pressure increases with r.p.m. and consequently increases the delivered weight of mixture, the h.p. required to pump each pound of mixture delivered, will decrease. The temperature rise of the

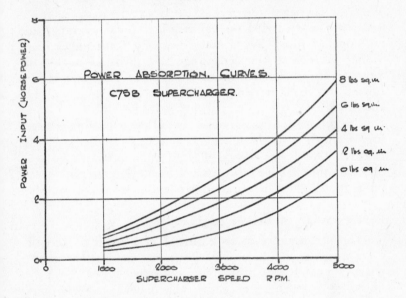

mixture delivered will also decrease (in relation to the quantity), for the same reason.

As there are moving parts in contact, inside the pumping chamber, it is necessary to feed lubricant thereto, and all oil supplied will eventually be transferred to the engine cylinders. The vane-type blower therefore requires a special type of metering device designed to feed the absolute minimum quantity of oil to the friction surfaces, and unaffected by pressure differences inside the casing.

Typical of the Roots-type blower is the Wade Ventor, manufactured by Wade Engineering Ltd. This is normally arranged for vee-rope drive from the engine crankshaft, the drive usually being combined with the existing dynamo-fan layout. Three-lobe rotors and skewed ports are employed to produce a pulsation-free delivery. The lubrication system comprises a tapping from the engine pressure-oil supply, taken via a fascia-mounted control valve to the gear chambers. The control valve is operated at intervals to replenish the chambers.

The Shorrock blower, made by Shorrock Superchargers Ltd., is the best-known example of a proprietary vane-type blower. Its internal construction is well illustrated by the diagrams on pages 189 and 263. It will be noted that the four vanes are carried on ball-bearings (two per vane) and are impelled round by the rotor drum itself, the angular and sliding movement between vanes and drum being accommodated by specially designed trunnions. The rotor itself is carried on ball bearings, and vee-rope drive is usually employed.

The lubrication system makes use of the engine pressure-oil supply which feeds the lower via a specially graded metering device. This device ensures that the minimum quantity of oil necessary for effective lubrication is used. No attention to the lubrication system is required while the blower is running.

Performance of blown engines

The performance to be expected as a result of adopting supercharging is adequately shown by the various curves, pages 264 and 265, which are reproduced by courtesy of Shorrock Superchargers Ltd. The following performance figures of two widely different types of car, with and without blower, are also interesting, the blower in each case being a Shorrock.

			Morris Minor (MM)		*M.G. Midget (TD)*	
			Unblown	Blown	Unblown	Blown
Top gear acceleration (secs.):						
10—30 m.p.h.	...	...	17.6	15.2	11.5	9.0
20—40 ,,	...	...	19.3	14.2	11.8	7.7
30—50 ,,	...	...	24.1	17.6	12.7	8.4
40—60 ,,	...	...	—	—	17.3	8.8
3rd gear acceleration (secs.):						
10—30 m.p.h.	...	...	10.2	9.8	7.8	6.8
20—40 ,,	...	...	12.1	9.1	7.7	6.0
30—50 ,,	...	...	—	—	8.9	6.0
40—60 ,,	...	...	—	—	—	6.0

Acceleration through gears (secs.):			Morris Minor (MM)		M.G. Midget (TD)	
			Unblown	Blown	Unblown	Blown
0—30 m.p.h.	...	...	8.7	7.0	5.5	4.2
0—40 ,,	...	...	15.1	12.2	9.0	6.5
0—50 ,,	...	...	34.2	14.3	13.5	9.4
0—60 ,,	...	...	—	—	21.3	11.7
0—70 ,,	...	...	—	—	—	17.2
B.h.p.	...	...	24.5	38.5	54.4	69.0
R.p.m.	...	...	4,400	4,400	5,200	5,200
M.p.g. (overall) ...	...	...	40.5	36.0	26.3	23.0
Comp. r. ...	...	...	6.6:1	6.6:1	7.3:1	7.3:1
Fuel (octane rating)	...	...	70—72	70—72	70—72	70—72

CHAPTER 25

Appendices

Definitions—Abbreviations—Useful constants and formulæ—
Design data of British competition engines—Directory of suppliers

Appendix 1

Definitions

SPECIFIC HEAT: The quantity of heat necessary to raise the temperature of a substance through 1 deg.

BRITISH THERMAL UNIT (B.Th.U.): The heat required to raise 1 lb. of a substance through 1 deg. F.

MECHANICAL EQUIVALENT OF HEAT (Joule's Equivalent): 1 B.Th.U. = 778 ft. lb.

CALORIFIC VALUE: The capacity of a substance for giving up heat when a mass of it is burnt. (Usually expressed as B.Th.U.s per lb.)

COMBUSTION: The combination of different chemical elements resulting in emission of heat.

CONDUCTION OF HEAT: The transfer of heat through a body from the hotter to the cooler part.

CONDUCTIVITY: The rate at which heat flows (in heat units per sec.) is directly proportional to the temperature difference between the two parts, and to the conductivity of the substance.

UNIT OF CONDUCTIVITY: The quantity of heat, in heat units, that flows per second across a face 1 sq. ft. in area for each degree of temperature drop per ft. of distance that the heat travels.

CONVECTION: Transfer of heat by virtue of the motion of the parts of heated bodies. The chief means of temperature equalization in liquids and gases. Cannot occur in solids.

RADIATION: Transfer of heat from a hot body to a cold one by waves of heat passing through the atmosphere.

ABSOLUTE TEMPERATURE: When temperature is changed by 1 deg. C. (constant pressure) the amount by which the gas expands in volume is 1/273 part of its volume at 0 deg. C. Therefore, at 273 deg. below 0 deg. C., the volume will be zero. Thus, absolute zero is 273 deg. C. Temperature reckoned therefrom is called Absolute Temperature, e.g., the boiling point of water (100 deg. C.), is 373 deg. C. absolute.

Abbreviations, etc.

Term.	Abbreviation.	Symbol.
Absolute	Abs. ...	—
British thermal unit	B.th.U. ...	—
Compression ratio	Comp. r. ...	r.

Term.					Abbreviation.		Symbol.
Efficiency ...	...	...	...	...	eff.	...	η
Efficiency, Mechanical	...	...	...	mech. eff.	...	$\eta m.$
Horse-power, Brake ...	...	...	...	b.h.p.	...	—
Horse-power, Indicated	...	...	...	i.h.p.	...	—
Joule ...	...	...	...	...	—	...	J.
Mean effective pressure	...	...	...	m.e.p.	...	—
Mechanical equivalent of heat	...	...	—	...	J.
Specific heat ...	...	...	...	...	sp. ht.	...	c.
,, ,, , at constant pressure ...	...	—	...	c_p
,, ,, , at constant volume ...	...	—	...	c_v
,, ,, , Ratio of	...	...	...	—	...	γ
Temperature	...	...	...	...	temp.	...	t.
,, , absolute	...	...	...	—	...	T or θ
Vacuum	...	...	...	...	vac.	...	—

Useful Constants and Formulae

Swept Volume of one cylinder $= \dfrac{3.14 \times D^2 \times S}{4}$ where

$$D = \text{cylinder bore; } S = \text{piston stroke.}$$

Compression ratio $= \dfrac{V + v}{v}$ where $V = $ swept volume.

$$v = \text{volume of space above piston at top of stroke.}$$

Piston speed in feet per min. $= 2 \times$ r.p.m. $\times$ stroke in feet

$$\text{or} = \frac{\text{r.p.m.} \times \text{stroke in inches}}{6}$$

$$\text{or} = \frac{\text{r.p.m.} \times \text{stroke in mm.}}{152.4}$$

B.h.p. $= \dfrac{PLAN}{33,000}$ where P = brake mean effective pressure in lb./sq. in.

L = length of stroke in feet.

A = area of one piston in square inches.

N = number of power strokes per minute.

B.m.e.p. lb./sq. in. $= \dfrac{\text{b.h.p.} \times 33,000}{LAN}$ for values of LAN, see above.

B.m.e.p. of 1,000-c.c. engine $= \dfrac{\text{b.h.p.} \times 13,125}{\text{r.p.m.}}$

For other capacities alter figure of 13,125 *pro rata*, i.e., for 2,000-c.c. engine use 26,250.

B.h.p. $= \dfrac{\text{r.p.m.} \times \text{torque in lb. ft.}}{5,250}$

T

$$\text{Torque in lb. ft.} = \frac{\text{b.m.e.p.} \times \text{volume in c.c.}}{2,473}$$

$$\text{M.p.h.} = \frac{\text{r.p.m.} \times \text{wheel dia. in inches}}{\text{gear ratio} \times 336}$$

Mean gas velocity through port in ft. per sec.

$$= \frac{\text{Piston speed}}{60} \times \frac{D^2}{d^2}$$

Mean gas velocity through valve in ft. per sec.

$$= \frac{\text{Piston speed}}{60} \times \frac{D^2 \times 22}{V \times L \times 7}$$

Where D = diameter of piston.
d = diameter of port.
V = diameter at throat of valve.
L = lift of valve.

Design Data of British Competition Engines

Make of Engine.	No. of cyls.	Bore and Stroke, mm.	Cubic capacity, c.c.	B.h.p. at r.p.m.	Max. torque at r.p.m. (lb. ft.)	Comp. ratio.
A.C.	6	65 / 100	1,991	85 / 4,500	105 / 2,750	7.5 : 1
Aston Martin	6	78 / 90	2,580	107 / 5,000	130 / 3,000	6.5 : 1
Bristol 401	6	66 / 96	1,971	85 / 4,500	107 / 3,500	7.5 : 1
Bristol 403	6	66 / 96	1,971	100 / 5,250	147 / 3,500	7.5 : 1
Ford " Prefect," 1952-3	4	63.5 / 92.5	1,172	31 / 4,000	46.4 / 2,400	6.16 : 1
Ford " Consul "	4	79.3 / 76.2	1,508	47 / 4,400	74 / 2,400	6.8 : 1
Ford " Zephyr "	6	79.3 / 76.2	2,262	68 / 4,000	112 / 2,000	6.8 : 1
Frazer-Nash	6	66 / 96	1,971	140 / 5,750	125.4 / 4,500	9 : 1
H.R.G.	4	73 / 89.4	1,496	65 / 4,800	71 / 4,800	7 : 1
Jaguar XK120	6	83 / 106	3,442	160 / 5,200	195 / 2,500	7 : 1
Jaguar XK120C	6	83 / 106	3,442	200 / 5,800	195 / 2,500	8 : 1
Jowett " Javelin "	4	72.5 / 90	1,486	52.5 / 4,500	76 / 2,600	7.2 : 1
Jowett " Jupiter "	4	72.5 / 90	1,486	62.5 / 4,500	84 / 3,000	7.6 : 1
Lea-Francis	4	85 / 110	2,496	100 / 4,000	142 / 2,500	7 : 1
M.G. TD	4	66.5 / 90	1,250	54.4 / 5,200	63.5 / 2,600	7.27 : 1
Morgan (Standard)	4	85 / 92	2,088	68 / 4,200	108 / 2,000	7.1 : 1
Morris MM	4	57 / 90	919	27.5 / 4,400	39 / 2,400	6.6 : 1
Riley	4	69 / 100	1,496	55 / 4,500	78 / 2,500	6.8 : 1
Riley	4	80.5 / 120	2,443	102 / 4,400	134 / 3,000	7.25 : 1
Sunbeam-Talbot	4	81 / 110	2,267	70 / 4,000	113 / 2,400	6.45 : 1
Sunbeam Alpine	4	81 / 110	2,267	80 / 4,200	124 / 1,800	7.42 : 1
Triumph TR 2	4	83 / 92	1,991	90 / 4,800	117 / 3,000	8.5 : 1

THE ABOVE TABLE DOES NOT NECESSARILY REPRESENT THE MAXIMUM PERFORMANCE OBTAINABLE

275

Appendix 3

Suppliers

This Appendix is obviously far from complete, but will serve as a guide to the location of specialist suppliers and others willing to undertake, or advise on, the class of work with which the enthusiast is concerned.

ALLOY CYLINDER HEADS (SIDE VALVE):
> Adlards Motors Ltd., 31, Acre Lane, London, S.W.2.
> The Aquaplane Company, Oulton Broad.
> V. W. Derrington Ltd., London Road, Kingston-on-Thames.

ALLOY CYLINDER HEADS (O.H.V.):
> Laystall Engineering Co. Ltd., 53, Gt. Suffolk Street, London, S.E.1.

BUILDING-UP WORN (HARDENED) PARTS:
> The British Oxygen Co. Ltd., Bridgewater House, Cleveland Drive, London, S.W.1 (and Branches).

CAMSHAFT REBUILDING AND MODIFYING:
> Leonard Reece, Carshalton, Surrey.

COMPRESSION RATIO ALTERATIONS (MACHINING FOR):
> Wm. Birch (Eng.) Ltd., Milton Street, Manchester 7.
> Lionel Leonard, 4, Morrish Road, London, S.W.2.

CONNECTING ROD AND PISTON BALANCING:
> Laystall Engineering Co. Ltd., 53, Gt. Suffolk Street, London, S.E.1.

CRACK TESTING:
> Laystall Engineering Co. Ltd., 53, Gt. Suffolk Street, London, S.E.1.

CRANKSHAFT BALANCING:
> The Aquaplane Company, Oulton Broad.
> Laystall Engineering Co. Ltd., 53, Gt. Suffolk Street, London, S.E.1.
> Lotus Engineering Co. Ltd., 7, Tottenham Lane, London, N.8.

ENGINE BENCH TESTING
> The Aquaplane Company, Oulton Broad.
> Laystall Engineering Co. Ltd., 53, Gt. Suffolk Street, London, S.E.1.

FLYWHEEL AND CLUTCH BALANCING:
> Laystall Engineering Co. Ltd., 53, Gt. Suffolk Street, London, S.E.1.
> Geo. Hartwell Ltd., Holdenhurst Road, Bournemouth.

FLYWHEEL LIGHTENING:
> The Aquaplane Company, Oulton Broad.
> Toulmin Motors, 343, Staines Road, Hounslow.

MANIFOLD AND DUAL-CARBURETTER SETS, ETC.:
> The Aquaplane Company, Oulton Broad.
> Buckler's, Caversham Road, Reading.
> Central Garage, High Street, Bangor, N. Wales.
> O. H. J. Davies, Castle Garage, Pembroke.
> Dellow Motors, Alvechurch, Birmingham.
> V. W. Derrington, Ltd., London Road, Kingston-on-Thames.
> Raymond Mays and Partners Ltd., Bourne, Lincs.
> Geo. Hartwell Ltd., Holdenhurst Road, Bournemouth.

SUPERCHARGER INSTALLATIONS:
> Carburetters Ltd., Grange Road, London, N.W.10.
> North Downs Eng. Co. Ltd., Westway, Caterham.
> Shorrock Superchargers Ltd., Fletchemsted Highway, Coventry.
> Wade Engineering Ltd., Gatwick Airport, Horley, Surrey.

VALVE MODIFICATIONS:
> Lotus Engineering Co. Ltd., 7 Tottenham Lane, London, N.8.

Appendix 4

Ford 10 performance figures

These figures have been supplied by Buckler's, of Reading; they represent the performance of Buckler Ford 10 Specials, having a weight of approximately 10 cwt., and have been obtained by owners using different degrees of engine tuning as indicated.

1,172-c.c. Formula. 8.5 : 1 Compression ratio. Copperized head. 5.5 : 1 Axle ratio. 7.98 2nd, 13.87 1st. Standard camshaft 4.50×17 Tyres.		Supercharged. Standard cam 4.7 Axle ratio. 6.8 2nd, 11.8 4.50 × 17 Tyres.	
Gears used.	Time.	Gears used.	Time.
	Secs.		*Secs.*
1st	4.5	1st	3.9
1st & 2nd	7.3	1st	5.2
1st & 2nd	10.0	1st & 2nd	7.5
1st, 2nd & 3rd	16.6	1st & 2nd	10.6
1st, 2nd & 3rd	27.0	1st & 2nd	14.3
—	—	1st, 2nd & 3rd	21.0
1st	3.5	1st	2.1
2nd	4.8	2nd	3.6
2nd	5.2	2nd	3.9
—	—	2nd	4.6
—	—	2nd	6.8
Top	6.9	Top	5.6
Top	6.9	Top	5.6
Top	7.8	Top	5.5
Top	10.2	Top	5.8
Top	13.0	Top	7.5
Top	—	Top	11.1
—	19.8	—	18.5
Gear ratio.	Maximum speed.	Gear ratio.	Maximum sp
Top	80 m.p.h.	Top	90–92 m.p.h.
2nd	60 m.p.h.	2nd	72 m.p.h.
1st	35 m.p.h.	1st	40 m.p.h.
Gear ratio.	Gradient climbable.	Gear ratio.	Gradient clim
1st	1 in 2.5 (20 m.p.h.)	1st	1 in 2.1
2nd	1 in 4.5	2nd	1 in 3.8
2nd	1 in 5.8	2nd	1 in 4.5
—	—	2nd	1 in 5.0
Top	1 in 8.0	Top	1 in 5.5
Top	1 in 20	Top	1 in 8.0

	8.5 : 1 Compression ratio—Copperized head. Axle ratio 4.7 : 1. 6.8 2nd and 11.8 1st Gear. 4-branch Exhaust and Twin S.U.s. Racing camshaft. 5.00 × 14 Tyres.		Ditto, but Axle ratio 5.5 : 1. 7.98 2nd and 13.87 1st Gear. 5.00 × 16 or 4.50 × 17 Tyres.
M.p.h.	Gears used.	Time.	Time.
		Secs.	*Secs.*
0—30	1st	3.4	3.1
0—40	1st	5.5	5.1
0—50	1st & 2nd	8.6	7.9
0—60	1st & 2nd	12.2	12.6
0—70	1st and 2nd	18.5	18.3
0—80	1st, 2nd & 3rd	28.8	—
10—30	1st	2.9	2.8
20—40	2nd	4.4	4.2
30—50	2nd	5.1	4.9
40—60	2nd	6.3	6.5
50—70	2nd	9.5	—
10—30	Top	6.2	5.9
20—40	Top	6.4	6.2
30—50	Top	6.5	6.3
40—60	Top	7.2	6.9
50—70	Top	9.2	9.0
60—80	Top	15.6	18.5
nding ¼ mile	—	19.3	18.8
	Gear ratio.	*Maximum speed.*	*Maximum speed.*
	Top	85/87 m.p.h.	80 m.p.h.
	2nd	70 m.p.h.	60 m.p.h.
	1st	40 m.p.h.	35 m.p.h.
M.p.h.	*Gear ratio.*	*Gradient climbable.*	*Gradient climbable.*
30	1st	1 in 2.5	1 in 2.3
30	2nd	1 in 4.0	1 in 3.5
50	2nd	1 in 6.0	1 in 5.0
60	2nd	1 in 7.3	—
50	Top	1 in 7.6	1 in 7.2
70	Top	1 in 10	1 in 9.2

SECTIONAL DRAWINGS OF ENGINES
(Described in text)

	Page
Aston Martin	116, 117, 118
Bristol	122
Ford " Consul "	133
Ford Ten	129
Ford " Zephyr "	135
Jaguar	140
Jowett	149
Lea-Francis	156
M.G.	160

SECTIONAL DRAWINGS OF ENGINES
(Not described in text)

	Page
Alvis 3-litre	49
Armstrong-Siddeley Sapphire	261
Austin A90	53
Morris Minor s.v.	267
Renault 750	268
Riley 2.5 litre	60
Singer 1500	59
Standard Vanguard	50
Sunbeam-Talbot 90	54

INDEX

A

A.C. engine, 58, 257
A.C. engine, tuning, 257
Accuracy, rocker, 198
Air, specific heat of, 17
Air standard efficiency, 21
"Aquaplane" modifications
    (Ford Ten), 219
Assembly, crankcase, Bristol,
    123
Assembly, crankcase, Ford Ten,
    128
Assembly, crankcase, Jaguar,
    139
Assembly, crankcase, Jowett,
    145
Assembly, crankshaft, Aston
    Martin, 114
Assembly, crankshaft, Ford
    "Consul" and "Zephyr,"
    134
Assembly, main, M.G., 159
Attention to the exhaust side,
    176
Attractive engine (Ford Ten),
    219
Auxiliary drives, general, 55
Auxiliary drives, Jaguar, 143
Auxiliary drives, Jowett, 150
Auxiliary drives, Lea-Francis,
    157
Auxiliary drives, M.G., 165

B

Balancing, problems of, 64
Balancing problems, sixes and
    eights, 68

Balancing, single-cylinder, 67
Basic materials, 47
Bearing location, 63
Bearings and materials, 61
Blown engines, performance,
    270
B.m.e.p. and torque, 27
Bore-stroke ratio, 69
Brake horse-power, 22
Breathing, 102
Buckler, Mr. C. D. F. (Ford
    tuning), 227

C

Calculating thermal efficiency,
    25
Cam followers, 201
Camshaft and valve gear,
    Bristol, 56, 124
Camshafts, special, Jaguar, 232
Carburetters, Jowett, 241
Casting, main, Lea-Francis,
    154
Chamber, combustion, 37, 76,
    98, 107
Charging, maximum, 37
Chassis modifications, Jaguar,
    236
Clearance volume, 37, 73
Clearances, exacting, piston,
    205
Coils and plugs, 112
Combustion chamber, 37, 76,
    98, 107
Comparison of types, super-
    chargers, 266
Compression ratio and detona-
    tion, 28

Compression ratio and heat loss, 31

Compression ratio and pressure increase, 30

Compression ratio, raising, 18, 219, 227, 230, 233, 240, 248, 257, 258, 259

Compression ratios, high, 28, 213

Connecting rods, accuracy of, 209

Correcting errors in connecting rods, 210

Crankcase assembly, Bristol, 123

Crankcase assembly, Ford Ten, 128

Crankcase assembly, Jaguar, 139

Crankcase assembly, Jowett, 145

Crankshaft assembly, Aston Martin, 114

Crankshafts, 63

Current, ignition, 111

Cylinder head and valve gear, Aston Martin, 116

Cylinder head and valve gear, Ford "Consul" and "Zephyr," 136

Cylinder head and valve gear, Jaguar, 141

Cylinder head and valve gear, M.G., 162

Cylinder head, Bristol, 56, 125

Cylinder head design, 73, 102

Cylinder heads and valve gear, Jowett, 147

D

Dampers, vibration, 69

Data, performance, 72

Davies, Mr. O. H. J. (Ford tuning), 230

Design, cylinder head, 73, 102

Design, piston, 209

Design, supercharger, 264

Detonation and compression ratio, 28

Drives, auxiliary, general, 55

Drives, auxiliary, Jaguar, 143

Drives, auxiliary, Jowett, 150

Drives, auxiliary, Lea-Francis, 157

Drives, auxiliary, M.G., 165

E

Efficiency, air standard, 21

Efficiency, mechanical, 23

Efficiency, thermal, 25

Efficiency, volumetric, 24, 25

Efficient scavenging, 75, 107

Engine, an attractive (Ford), 219

Engines, blown, performance of, 270

Equipment, racing, "Aquaplane" (Ford), 226

Errors, correcting, in connecting rods, 210

Exacting clearances (piston), 205

Exhaust pipe layout, 46, 195

Exhaust pressure, 37

Exhaust side, attention to the, 176

Exhaust systems, 46, 195, 222, 230, 234

Expansion and compression, 19

Expansion pressure, factors governing, 24

F

Factors governing expansion pressure, 24
Failure, fatigue, 51
Fatigue failure, 51
First principles, heat engines, 16
Five-stage tuning (M.G.), 247
Flat-four engine (Jowett), 145
Followers, cam, 201
Forced induction, 262
Forces, secondary (balancing), 66
Ford o.h.v. engines, tuning, 257
Ford Ten engine, tuning, 219

G

Gas flow, considerations of, 80
Gas leakage (pistons), 206
Gas velocity and valve size, 34, 104
General points, cylinder head design, 73

H

Head design, cylinder, 73
Head volume, obtaining, 214
Heat loss, 31
Heat loss and compression ratio, 76
Heat of air, specific, 17
High compression ratios, 28, 213
High-speed operation, engine, 40
Horse-power, brake, 22
Horse-power, indicated, 22

I

Ignition current, 111
Ignition systems, 112
Improving performance, 102, 170
Improving volumetric efficiency, 105
Inclined overhead valves, 56
Indicated horse-power, 22
Induction, forced, 262
Influence of plug position, 109
Inlet ports, 105
Inlet tract, 102
Inlet valve size, 104

J

Jaguar engine tuning, 232
Jowett engine tuning, 238
Jowett flat-four engine, 145

L

Leakage, gas, 207
Lightening, rockers, 200
Lightening, tappets, 204
Location, crankshaft bearings, 63
Loss, heat, 31

M

Materials, in engine construction, 47
Maximum charging, 37
Mechanical efficiency, 26
M.G. engine tuning, 247
Modifications, valve timing, 201
Morris Minor s.v., tuning, 258

N

Non-ferrous metals in engine construction, 48

O

Objects of forced induction, 262
Obtaining head volume, 214
O.h. inlet and side exhaust valves, 97
O.h.c., double, layout, 57
O.h.c., single, layout, 58
O.h.v. head, turbulence features, 78
O.h.v., inclined, combustion chamber, 98
O.h.v. layouts, 76
Operation, high-speed engine, 40
Operation, valve, 55
Overlap, valve, snags, 39
Oversize valves, 175

P

Performance, blown engines, 270
Performance data, engine, 72
Performance, improving, 102, 170
Piston design, 209
Piston rings, 206
Pistons, special, 209, 217
Plug, spark, position of, 109
Plugs and coils, 112
Port characteristics, inlet, 105
Power production, 28
Pressure, exhaust, 37
Pressure increase, with compression ratio, 30
Pressure, pulsating, exhaust, 41

Problems of balancing, 64
Pulsating pressure, exhaust, 41

R

R4 Jowett engine, 150
Racing equipment, "Aquaplane" (Ford), 219
Raising compression ratio, 18, 219, 227, 230, 233, 240, 248, 257, 258
Ratio, bore-stroke, 69
Requirements, combustion chamber, 75, 107
Rings, piston, 206
Rocker shaft details, 199
Rocker, valve, accuracy, 198
Rods, connecting, 209

S

Scavenging, exhaust, 41
Secondary forces (balancing), 66
Shaft, rocker, 199
Side exhaust and o.h. inlet valve layout, 97
Single-cylinder (balancing), 67
Single o.h.c. layout, 58
Six-stage tuning (Ford), 221
Sixes and eights (balancing), 68
Spark plug position, 109
Special pistons, 209, 217
Specific heat of air, 17
Springs and collars, valve, 193
Sprint racing (Ford), 230
Sunbeam-Talbot, tuning, 258
Supercharger design, 264
Supercharger performance, 270
Superchargers, comparison of types, 266

Systems, exhaust, 46, 195, 222, 230, 234

T

Tappets, lightening, 204
Temperature, water, 33
Thermal efficiency, 25
Timing, valve, 36
Timing, valve, modifications to, 201
Torque and b.m.e.p., 27
Tract, inlet, 102
Tuning in five stages (M.G.), 247
Tuning in six stages (Ford), 221
Turbulence, 34
Turbulence features with o.h.v. head, 78

V

Valve layouts, o.h., 76
Valve operation, 55
Valve size, inlet, 104
Valve timing, 36
Valve timing, modifications to, 201
Valves, clearance to pistons, 216
Valves, oversize, 175
Valves, springs and collars, 193
Vibration dampers, crankshaft, 69
Volume, cylinder head, determining, 214
Volumetric efficiency, 24, 25

W

Water temperature, 33